Legends
of the
Spanish Southwest

The Garden of Tubac

Reproduced from old plans, drawings, and descriptions

LEGENDS OF THE SPANISH SOUTHWEST

by
CLEVE HALLENBECK
Author of Spanish Missions of the Old Southwest
and
JUANITA H. WILLIAMS

THE ARTHUR H. CLARK COMPANY
Glendale, California, U.S.A.
1938

Contents

Illustrations

Map

Foreword

Foreword

The colonization of our Atlantic seaboard and of our southwest were practically contemporaneous, and the courage, faith, and endurance displayed by the English in conquering the wilderness of New England were not greater nor more steadfast than those shown by the Spanish in facing and overcoming the hazards of the inhospitable southwest.

The New England people preserved little of the romance of that period. But the Spanish pioneers, while as practical as were their nordic brothers, were a poetic people, and the one lone flower of romance that we find in New England's colonial history can be matched by a whole garden of flowers garnered from the Spanish period of our southwest. Even the Acadian story of immortal Evangeline cannot be ranked in heart interest above the California story of Concepción Arguello, or the Texas story of Juan Huisar.

We have chosen from the wealth of material available only such of the old Spanish legends as were, in our opinion, most worthy to survive as a part of our national literature. Limitations of space made it necessary for us to reject a number of meritorious legends, and it was deemed advisable to omit some that have been published before or are well known, in order to preserve others that to date are practically unknown except in the districts where their scenes are said to have been enacted.

Several of the stories appear to be historically verifiable. Others doubtless are more or less fanciful, although probably even the supposedly fictional ones have a substantial foundation of fact.

In such of the legends as were susceptible to presentation according to short-story technique, we have added appropriate details, dialogue, and setting. But our self-imposed task carried certain obligations, and one of these was to refrain from altering the story itself. This necessitated our preserving any prejudice or error found in a legend, whether such met our approval or not. Explanatory matter preceding or following the body of a legend is a part thereof, except where it bears our initials.

We believe that the character of a people may be more clearly reflected in its legendary lore than in the recital of its political history, and it is our hope that these stories will reveal somewhat of the true character of the Spanish pioneers of our southwest.

CLEVE HALLENBECK
JUANITA H. WILLIAMS

Roswell, New Mexico, 1938

Introduction

Introduction

The following brief outline of Spain's activities in our southwest is offered to those of our readers who may not be acquainted with the early history of this region, but who may desire a connected historical background for the legends that follow.

Spain's objective, during the three centuries covered by her new world activities, was to create a great overseas empire under the rule of the crown and the spiritual domination of the Roman catholic church; an empire not primarily of Spanish people, but of civilized, christianized indian subjects.

It was a magnificent dream, but one impossible of realization, and it contributed largely to Spain's eventual bankruptcy. She financed most of the exploring, colonizing, and missionary enterprises which were spread over the West Indies, most of South America, Central America, western North America, and the Philippine islands, and some of these activities were astonishingly expensive. Much has been written of the riches of gold and silver taken by Spain from the new world, but her income from this source gradually decreased, while her expenditures as gradually increased, throughout the colonial period. The crown claimed but one-fifth of the gold and silver mined, and did not always receive that much of it.

Spain's occupation of continental North America began with the *entrada* of Hernando Cortez into

Mexico in 1519. His capture of the Aztec stronghold of Tenochtitlan (now Mexico City) was but the beginning of the real conquest of Mexico. Mexico at that time was peopled by a number of more or less related tribes, many of which were held in subjection by the Aztecs. At first these subject tribes welcomed Cortez as a savior.

Mexico City, built by Cortez and his successors,[1] formed a base from which expeditions were sent out in all directions. Cortez founded Zacatula on the west coast in 1522, and there fitted out several maritime expeditions for northward exploration. None of these, however, got as far north as the present limits of the United States. In this enterprise Cortez was greatly handicapped by the machinations of his old enemy, Nuño de Guzmán, who had conquered Nueva Galicia (roughly corresponding to modern Sinaloa) in 1529, and who ruled that province until removed in 1536.

In 1535 Mexico (then called Nueva España) was made a viceregal domain with Antonio de Mendoza the first viceroy. Under his able administration, which lasted until 1550, the entire region southward from Mexico City to Central America was occupied, a university was established, printing presses were imported and books published, half a dozen towns were built on the Pacific coast, and many schools for the Indians were founded.

Occupation of the territory northward from Mexico City was rather slow, but before the end of the sixteenth century spear-heads of settlement were being thrust

---

[1] The building that often is referred to as the palace of the Montezumas is in reality the viceregal palace, begun by Cortez and finished by Mendoza. The residence of the native war-chief (the Montezuma) was hardly more than a mud hut.

northeastward toward Texas, northward toward New
Mexico, and northwestward toward Arizona. Pañuco
near the east coast, San Bartolomé in the Conchos
valley, and Culiacán near the west coast were at that
time the points of the three spear-heads.

The first Europeans to enter any part of our southwest were Alvar Nuñez (known in history as Cabeza
de Vaca [2]) and his three companions – the sole survivors of Narvaez's expedition that sailed from Spain
in 1527 for the conquest of Florida. These four men,
stranded on the coast of Texas and captured by the
Indians, after six years of slavery escaped and made
their way from tribe to tribe across western Texas,
southern New Mexico, southern Arizona and Sonora,
reaching the Spanish settlement at Culiacán in the
spring of 1536.

While in northern Sonora Nuñez had been told by
the Indians of populous villages to the north: these
probably were either the seven Moqui pueblos or the
Zuñi group of six pueblos, the former being in northeastern Arizona and the latter in west-central New
Mexico. The imagination of the idle class in Mexico
at once identified these villages with the fabled Seven
Cities of Cibola, [3] and in 1538 the viceroy sent Fray
Marcos de Niza, accompanied by one of Nuñez's three
companions, Estevanico, [4] and an escort of Indians, to
reconnoiter the villages of which Nuñez had heard.

---

[2] The title, Cabeza de Vaca, means head of a cow, and was conferred on
an ancestor of Nuñez on the distaff side, for having marked with the skull
of a cow a pass through the mountains, whereby a christian army was en-
abled to surprise and defeat a moorish force in what is recorded in history
as the battle of Las Navas de Tolosa (1212).

[3] See legend of "The gran quivira."

[4] While Estevanico is usually spoken of as a Negro, Nuñez plainly recorded that he was an Arab.

These Indians conducted Marcos toward the Zuñi pueblos, and when about halfway there Marcos stopped and sent Estevanico on ahead to examine the country and send back reports thereon.

Estevanico reached one of the Zuñi pueblos (Kiakima, according to the Zuñians; Hawikuh, according to the historians) where he and part of his indian escort were killed. The rest fled back to Marcos with the news. Thereupon he, approaching with caution, got a distant view of the pueblo of Hawikuh with its adobe terraces burnished by the rays of the setting sun, and hastened back to Mexico with a report that did credit to his imagination.

A careful perusal of his written report convinces us that Marcos did not intentionally fabricate evidence. But it raised to a high pitch the interest of the floating population of Mexico, and in 1540 a well-equipped expedition under Francisco Vasquez de Coronado was dispatched northward from Compostela.[5]

The Coronado expedition traveled through southern Arizona, New Mexico, northwestern Texas, and on into eastern Kansas, and then, thoroughly disillusioned, turned back reaching Mexico City in 1542.

This damped enthusiasm among the fortune-hunters of Mexico, and for nearly 40 years no more *entradas* were made into our southwest. In 1580 one Chamuscado, with a few soldiers [6] and three priests, went up into New Mexico, where the priests remained. Espejo, following up the Grande river two years later to bring

[5] A fuller account of Coronado's expedition, as far as the Rio Grande, will be found in the legend "La jornada del muerte."

[6] The first man to leave his autograph upon the celebrated Inscription Rock in western New Mexico was one of Chamuscado's officers, named Romero.

the priests back to Mexico, found that they had been killed by the Indians. Thereupon Espejo and eight of his men made a remarkable exploring tour of eastern Arizona and northern and eastern New Mexico before returning to Mexico.

He was followed in 1590 by de Sosa who conducted a swarm of colonists into northern New Mexico, intent upon founding a settlement. But he had undertaken this enterprise without authorization from the viceroy, so he shortly after was arrested and taken to Mexico City, his colonists trailing along behind.

This brings us up to the founding of New Mexico.

NEW MEXICO

The distinction of having founded the first white settlement in our southwest, and the second within the limits of the United States, belongs to Juan de Oñate, a wealthy miner of Zacatecas, a seasoned frontiersman, and a member of a family prominently identified with the history of western Mexico.

Oñate himself partly financed the large colonizing expedition that he led up the Rio Grande in the spring of 1598, and it cost its backers about one million dollars before it ever moved. Oñate settled on a beautiful site, at the confluence of the Chama and Grande rivers – and there founded the town of San Gabriel, his colonists finding temporary quarters in the abandoned indian pueblo of Yunque-Yunque.

The region entered by these colonists was occupied by sedentary Indians of six linguistic families: the Tehuas, Picuries, Cuares, Tanos, and Jemez, whose pueblos were scattered over the upper Grande watershed, and the Tompiros,[7] east of the Manzaño mountains. These six tribes were closely related ethnically. To the pueblo-dwelling tribes must be added the Zuñis, of west-central New Mexico and the Moquis, of northeastern Arizona, whose relationship to the other six is not definitely known.

These Indians were primarily agricultural, supplementing their farming activities with some hunting. They had a complicated religion, deep-rooted in their lives, and their government was purely democratic, each pueblo being an independent unit.

With a single exception, all the pueblos received the Spaniards amicably — outwardly, at least — and took the oath of allegiance, through their chiefs, to the crown of Spain. The one exception, "sky-dwelling" Acoma, held aloof, and later massacred a squad of soldiers who visited that pueblo. Thereupon Vincente Zaldivar, one of Oñate's captains and brother of the leader of the murdered squad, marched against Acoma with only 70 men and nearly annihilated the pueblo. This overwhelming defeat of the most nearly impregnable of the pueblos served to keep the others quiet for the ensuing half-century.

Santa Fe [8] was founded and made the capital in 1606, Oñate being the first governor. Oñate, besides being a successful colonizer, was an indefatigable explorer, and in addition to a thorough exploration of northern New Mexico, he conducted expeditions clear to the Gulf of California and up into Colorado and Kansas.

---

[7] The Piros, sometimes mentioned as a seventh tribe, were a branch of the Tompiros and spoke the same language.

[8] The exact year of the founding of Santa Fe has not been definitely established but 1606 is favored. The full name of this town was La Ciudad de la Santa Fé de San Francisco.

Additional colonists arrived from Mexico from time to time, and little towns began to appear along the upper Grande river and its tributaries. During the years 1625 to 1630 the mission field was extended to include the Tompiros, the Zuñis and the Moquis. Rebellious Acoma also at this time consented to fall in line and receive a white teacher.

The next event of importance in the history of New Mexico is the Pueblo rebellion of 1680 – one of the most disastrous indian uprisings ever staged within the limits of the United States. At this time there were 26 missions in as many pueblos, with some 64 secondary establishments (visitas),[9] served by 50 priests and having about 60,000 nominal indian adherents.

This revolt, in which 34 of the pueblos were involved, was caused primarily by the interference of the Spanish with the pagan religion of the natives. Secretly organized by the indian priests, who were bitterly hostile to christianity, with one Po-pé the dominant spirit, the blow fell suddenly in august, 1680, and had it not been for warnings given two days previously by some friendly Indians, not a Spaniard would have escaped. As it was, all were slain except those who succeeded in reaching Santa Fe or Isleta. These survivors, after a sanguinary battle at Santa Fe, retreated down the Rio Grande to El Paso del Norte.[10]

After attempts by others to reconquer the province had failed, Diego de Vargas accomplished the reconquest in 1692-1693. De Vargas was a humane, tactful man, and most of the pueblos submitted peaceably to him. The irreconcilable ones concentrated their forces

[9] A visita – also called asistencia – was a mission having no resident priest.
[10] A settlement was made on the present site of El Paso in 1681, but the original El Paso del Norte (now Juarez, Mexico) was founded in 1652.

at Santa Fe, which place De Vargas captured in a two-day fight.

A second revolt of the more refractory pueblos occurred in 1696, but it was speedily suppressed. Finding that De Vargas, who now was governor, really kept his promises, the Pueblo Indians gave no further trouble. Many of the former missions were rebuilt and a few new ones were established, and for three-fourths of a century nothing of note is to be recorded except almost continuous offensive and defensive operations of the Spanish and the Pueblo Indians against the Apaches, Comanches, Utes, and Navajos. Albuquerque [11] was founded in 1706 and named after the then viceroy, the Duke of Alburquerque. Other small towns were established here and there, but mostly along the trail leading to Mexico City. This road, nearly 2000 miles long, was in use as a highway for two and one-half centuries before any Anglo-american ever traversed it, but its long history of war, romance, adventure, and tragedy never has been written.

In the late 1770's the pressure of the Apaches and Comanches upon the northern frontier became so serious that the provinces of Texas, New Mexico, and Sonora (including what is now Arizona) were separated from the viceregality and put under a special government, and measures were taken to suppress the nomadic savages. The celebrated indian fighter, Juan Bautista de Anza, was sent from Arizona to New Mexico to take charge of the situation there. He began by thoroughly defeating the Comanches, on the plains of Kansas, killing their celebrated chieftain, Cuerno

---

11 The full name was San Felipe de Alburquerque. The first "r" was dropped from the name prior to the year 1779.

Verde,[12] with his own hand. Next, by a master stroke of diplomacy, he made the Comanches and the Navajos his allies against the Apaches, and soon had them with their backs to the wall.

With the Comanche and Apache menaces removed, the Spanish population increased more rapidly and by the end of the century numbered about 30,000.

From the year 1763 to the end of the century, all the territory west of the Mississippi belonged to Spain, and the Spanish governors at Santa Fe claimed, and exercised as far as they were able, suzerainty over the entire region. Much of Colorado was explored, and exploring expeditions penetrated northeastward to the Missouri river and northward to Yellowstone park.

In 1805 the first Anglo-americans, Zebulon M. Pike and his party, entered New Mexico. Pike's bearing while in New Mexico and Mexico was not calculated to win the friendship of the Spaniards.[13]

In 1810 New Mexico was granted a delegate to the Spanish *cortes* (parliament) and was the only one of the provinces of Spain's frontier ever to be accorded this distinction.

After Mexico won her independence from Spain in 1822, the people of New Mexico were for the first time taxed. Otherwise they were neglected. Duties on goods coming up from Mexico were so high that a thriving trade soon was built up between Santa Fe and the United States, over the route that became famous as the Santa Fe trail. So important did this commerce be-

---

[12] The name Cuerno Verde (green horn) was given by the Spaniards to this chief because of the green-painted buffalo horns he wore in his head-dress. Those horns still are in existence.

[13] Dr. R. E. Twitchell in *Leading facts of New Mexican history* (I, 476) criticises Pike rather severely, as do several other writers of the southwest.

come that the United States established a consulate at
Santa Fe in 1825.

There was a good deal of friction between New
Mexico and Mexico, with one or two small rebellions,
although Mexico, torn by rival factions and without
funds, was unable to administer the affairs of her frontier provinces efficiently. So when in 1846 General
Kearny appeared with an army of United States troops,
he met practically no resistance. It is said that most of
the pure-blood Spaniards remaining in the province
desired the change of flags.

After Kearny's departure for California, there was
a revolt of the Taos Indians aided by the Mexicans of
the Taos valley, and several Anglo-americans, including Governor Bent, were killed before Kearny's lieutenant, Colonel Price, arrived on the scene and crushed
the revolt.

A number of interesting monuments of the Spaniard
still are to be seen. Most of these are in Santa Fe, and
this ancient city of the Holy Faith itself, with its
quaint architecture, narrow, winding streets and castilian tongue, is about the only bit of colonial Spain
remaining to us. Among the most noteworthy monuments there are the *palacio de los gobernadores* (palace
of the governors) the churches of San Miguel and
Guadalupe, and the Rosario chapel.

The governors' palace, fronting one whole side of
the historic old plaza, is one story in height. It is said
to have had a tower at each end originally – certainly
the ends were designed to support towers – but these
have disappeared. Otherwise the building looks about
as it must have looked three centuries ago. This venerable structure has housed 103 governors, beginning

with Oñate in 1606 and ending with Curry in 1909. Of some 60 governors who ruled from here during the Spanish period, all but one were of the aristocracy of New Spain. This building now is used as a historical and archaeological museum, and it houses a great wealth of material.

The church of San Miguel was erected early in the seventeenth century for the use of a colony of Tlascalan Indians who had accompanied Oñate's expedition in 1598. Their settlement was just south of the Santa Fe river, and was called Analco. The interior woodwork of this church was burned in 1680, and repairs, begun in 1693, were finished in 1710. Within recent years the exterior has been plastered with concrete and reinforced with buttresses. This little church contains four very old and reputedly valuable paintings, one of which is said to be a genuine Cimabue.[14] Underneath the choir loft is a fine old bell, cast in 1356, that has a more romantic history than any other bell in America. The illustrious Diego de Vargas, who died while serving as governor of New Mexico, is buried near the altar of this church.[15]

The Rosario chapel, which was erected about 1695 by De Vargas, in fulfillment of a vow made during his campaign of 1693, has been largely rebuilt, and is of interest mainly because of its historical associations.[16]

[14] However, the present custodian of the San Miguel church assured the writers that underneath the lower frame of this picture is the name "Correggio." We cannot accept it as a genuine Cimabue – it is too well done. Possibly it is a copy of a Correggio.

[15] The record of the burial of De Vargas states only that he was buried in "the principal church." This is taken by some students to mean the church of San Francisco. But that church, which was destroyed in 1680, was not rebuilt until 1713-1714. De Vargas died in 1704.

16. See the legend "La conquistadora."

The church of Guadalupe, erected about 1640, is cruciform in shape and is the largest of the three. It also has been extensively remodeled in recent times, but it still contains its rare old paintings.

Several of the old mission churches in various indian pueblos are noteworthy because of their great age or other associations, but architecturally they are without merit. Among the most interesting ones are those at Acoma, Cochití, and Isleta. In Albuquerque, we find the old San Felipe cathedral, erected more than two centuries ago.

Scattered along the road down the Grande valley – the three-century-old road leading to Mexico City – are Spanish towns one and one-half to three centuries old – Peralta, Bernalillo, Los Lunas, Tomé, Belen, San Acacia, San Antonio, Socorro, San Marcial – nearly every one of which has its ancient church and time-eaten cemetery with quaint, old-world headstones, and the older graves marked only by little mounds of granite or marble dust. Also along that forgotten road are the fast-disappearing remains of many Spanish towns of which only the names are remembered, and of still others whose names even have been forgotten. Some of these were wiped out of existence by the Apaches and Comanches; others were abandoned from time to time (chiefly in the early 1780's) for better sites.

Texas

Spain apparently forgot all about her claim to the fertile domain of Texas – potentially the richest of all her possessions – until the Frenchman, La Salle, built a fort near Matagorda Bay in 1685. La Salle's modest plan was to collect an army of 4000 Indians, in addition to his 100 Frenchmen, and with these conquer not only Texas, but New Mexico and Nueva Vizcaya (modern Chihuahua and Durango). In this design he was abetted by the French king who placed four warships at his disposal.

According to Bancroft, La Salle's 100 men were "the scum of the French towns, to which were added 30 'gentlemen adventurers,' a few artisans and servants, a few families of colonists and a number of girls seeking husbands, with three priests, one a brother of La Salle."

By 1688 the colony had gone utterly to pieces; disease, starvation, and hostile Indians having done the work. A few of the Frenchmen had deserted to the Indians from time to time, and some of these later were found and rescued by the Spaniards.

When word of La Salle's invasion reached Spain, the viceroy in Mexico was instructed to oust him and establish Spanish outposts in Texas. Accordingly, in 1689 a Captain de Leon was dispatched with a small force into Texas. He reached Matagorda Bay, but did not find La Salle's fort, and for some reason returned to Mexico without having fulfilled any part of his commission. He was sent back the following year with a larger force; this time he found La Salle's fort, but found no Frenchmen. He then went on into eastern Texas where he established three missions, leaving them in charge of Fray Damian Manzanet (also spelled Masanet) two other friars, and a few soldiers; these he deemed sufficient to hold Texas against the French.

But owing to the great difficulty of transporting supplies from Mexico to eastern Texas, the outposts were abandoned three years later, and for 23 years Texas remained unoccupied.

In 1705 the French trader, Saint-Denis – one of the most picturesque characters in the early history of Texas – crossed from Louisiana to the presidio of San Juan, on the Rio Grande, ostensibly on a trading journey. In 1713, accompanied by some of the Indians of eastern Texas, he repeated his visit to San Juan. But this time he was taken into custody by the commandant of the presidio, Diego Ramón, and sent to Mexico City for examination. Being a Frenchman, he was able to give a plausible excuse for his trespass, and he was released on the condition that he guide a Spanish expedition into eastern Texas. This he did, and the expedition, under Captain Domingo Ramón (son of the commandant at San Juan) got under way in 1716, and eventually reached the upper San Antonio river in Texas. Incidentally, at the Nueces river, there was a wedding in this expedition – the first white wedding in Texas. This was in may, 1716.

' On the San Antonio river Ramón established the Bexar presidio [17] and, within a musket-shot of it, the mission of San Antonio de Valero. This is regarded by many writers as the beginning of the city of San Antonio. Leaving a company of soldiers at Bexar, Ramón next proceeded on into eastern Texas, reestablished the missions that had been abandoned in 1693, and erected the presidio of Nuestra Señora de los Dolores de Tejas. From there Lieutenant Diego Ramón (son of Captain Domingo Ramón and grandson of

[17] A Spanish presidio was more than a mere military post. Most of the soldiers were married men with families, and often they did farming and stock-raising in addition to their military duties. One presidio inspector complained that the soldiers of the Bexar presidio were so busy with farming that they neglected to mount guard. In addition, there often was a considerable civilian population clustered about the presidio.

Commandant Diego Ramón) with Saint-Denis went on to Mobile, returning later with a large consignment of merchandise and supplies.

After leaving the necessary priests and soldiers, the expedition then returned to Mexico.

War opened between Spain and France in 1719, and the French of Louisiana under Saint-Denis (who now was in command of the French outpost at Natchitoches, Louisiana) drove the Spanish out of eastern Texas, capturing two of them and confiscating the mission poultry. The next year a well-equipped expedition from Mexico under the Marqués de Aguayo, in turn drove out the French, and reoccupied the missions and presidio in eastern Texas.

The Marqués de Aguayo also in 1720 established the mission of San José de Aguayo in the San Antonio valley, two leagues below the Valero, but it was not completed until 1731.

In 1721 we have the first authentic record of supplies being sent to Texas by water. In that year a consignment of provisions, consisting mostly of "200 mule loads of flour," reached Matagorda Bay from Vera Cruz. After this, ships frequently touched at Matagorda Bay, near which both a presidio and a mission had been established.

The settlements in eastern Texas did not prosper, owing to the great difficulty of transporting supplies to that region. In 1730 and 1731 both missions and settlers were transferred, the former to the San Antonio valley and the latter, first to the Trinity river, and later to the valley of the San Antonio. The settlers, however, were dissatisfied with their new location, and eventually were permitted to return to their old homes.

The Indians of that portion of Texas occupied by the Spaniards were of several linguistic groups, but much alike in their other habits. They were semi-sedentary, but practiced little if any agriculture, subsisting mainly upon such animal and vegetable food as nature provided. They did a good deal of hunting, and in the coastal districts fish and other sea-food formed an important item of their diet.

These Indians received the Spaniards amicably, and little friction developed between the two races at any time. While lazy, the natives seemed to be intelligent, and under Spanish tutelage they became good artisans and farmers.

To the west, northwest, and north, however, the country was occupied by the Wichitas, Comanches, and Apaches, and with one or another of these the Spaniards were frequently in conflict.

The real growth of San Antonio and of the region thereabouts began with the arrival in 1731 of a consignment of colonists from the Canary islands. These newcomers were of good quality, and many citizens of Texas proudly trace their descent from these first families. The Canary islanders founded the villa of San Fernando, a short distance from the Bexar presidio. This villa eventually developed into the city of San Antonio, but during the Spanish period it was known as San Fernando.

For 30 years San Fernando prospered, and additional settlers came into Texas, most of them locating in the San Antonio valley, which became almost entirely taken up with large haciendas.

Additional presidios, with companion missions, were established at San Saba and San Luis Amarillas in the

1750's, but after a few years San Saba was sacked by the Comanches and both establishments were soon thereafter abandoned. There are local traditions of other outpost settlements in Texas, concerning which we have found no authentic record.

Disaster overtook the San Antonio valley in 1783 when an unnamed epidemic, which we suspect was yellow fever, carried off a large percentage of both Spaniards and Indians. From this blow neither San Fernando nor the missions ever entirely recovered; the latter continued to decline until 1794, when they were secularized and so ceased to exist as missions.

The general campaign against the Comanches and Apaches, which we mentioned in our sketch of New Mexico, relieved the Texas settlements from harassment, and the province seemed again on the road to prosperity. But this resurgence was short-lived. Before the end of the century another decline set in and from this there was no recovery. San Antonio was taken and retaken during the Mexican revolution, and was left in a sad state at the end of that conflict.[18]

After 1824 many Anglo-americans came into Texas, lured by the liberal land grants offered by Mexico, and by 1834 these outnumbered the Mexicans. (After Mexico had won her independence, the Spaniards were expelled from her dominions. Some went to Spain, some to the West Indies, and a few to the United States.)

18 It is not to be assumed that the San Antonio described by the first Anglo writers, in the 1830's and 1840's, was like the Spanish town of the preceding century. "Bexar (San Antonio) the ancient capital of Texas, now presents a sorrowful and gloomy picture. . . Her schools are neglected, her churches desolate, the sounds of human industry are almost hushed, and the voice of gladness and prosperity is converted into wailing and lamentations by the disheartening and multiple evils which surround the defenseless population." [From a petition sent to the government of Mexico in 1833.]

A change in the attitude of the Mexican government toward immigrants resulted in several oppressive laws aimed at the Anglo-american settlers, the most objectionable of which, to them, was a law prohibiting slavery in any Mexican territory. The Anglo colonists rebelled in 1835 and captured San Antonio late in that year. The town was retaken by Antonio Lopez (Santa Anna) the following spring, and the garrison, which had moved to and fortified the courtyard of the Valero mission (the Alamo) was defeated and the survivors put to the sword. Another force of several hundred Texans at Goliad met the same fate.

Shortly afterward Lopez, pursuing another Texas force under Sam Houston, was trapped on the San Jacinto river and completely defeated, Lopez himself being captured. This practically ended Texas's war for independence, although it was not acknowledged by Mexico for ten years thereafter.

Texas claimed the territory southward and westward to the Rio Grande, including the Spanish settlements east of that stream in New Mexico, although the Medina river (the longest tributary of the San Antonio river) was generally supposed to be the boundary between Texas and Coahuila. One old map shows both Coahuila and Nuevo Leon extending up into what is now Texas.

The only noteworthy monuments of the Spanish period remaining in Texas are the five missions of the San Antonio valley and the old San Fernando church – now a cathedral – in San Antonio.

The Valero mission, of which only the chapel minus its twin towers and dome remains, was named Alamo by a Spanish garrison that occupied it in 1804. It had been abandoned as a mission in 1763. The battle of the Alamo took place in the mission courtyard and in a long, cloistered building that had contained the shops and storerooms of the mission. The latter has disappeared, while the former now is occupied with business buildings.

A league below the Valero lies the mission Concepción. Little of it remains except the church, which is in a fair state of preservation. Many little legends cluster about this ancient institution.

A league below the Concepción lie the ruins of the San José, architecturally inferior to none except the San Xavier of Arizona. It was the residence of the *padre presidente* of the Texas mission field. It and the Valero are the only missions within the United States that boasted two-story cloisters.

The remaining two – the San Juan and the San Francisco – located, respectively, one and two leagues from the San José, are also quite interesting, but never were as important as the other three. Architecturally, these two are inferior.

The San Fernando church, said to have been begun in 1731, has been incorporated into the present San Fernando cathedral in San Antonio, but its outlines can still be made out.

ARIZONA

Arizona is the only one of our four southwestern states that was not organized and named as a province under the Spanish regime. Its settlements formed the northern frontier of the province of Sonora, which extended to the Gila river. The region between the Altar and Gila rivers was known as Pimeria Alta, and the name Pimeria should have been given to the present state of Arizona. As it is, this state was named after an obscure indian village in northern Sonora.

The mission of Los Angeles de Guevavi (The Angels of Guevavi) the first Spanish establishment within the present state of Arizona, was founded by Eusebio Kino [19] in 1692 in the Santa Cruz valley near the southern boundary of this state. This was followed by the San José de Tumacacori in 1697 and the San Xavier del Bac in 1700. These were the first of a never-finished chain that Kino desired to establish between Sonora and California so as to reach the latter province, still unoccupied at the time, by an overland route. Kino was a jesuit, and these were the only jesuitic missions ever established by the Spanish within our borders.[20] All others were under the franciscans (order of friars minor also known as the seraphic order).

These missions were mostly in the territory of the Papagos, but the Pimas and Yumas were at least next-door neighbors. The Indians of that region were sedentary, and lived in villages except in the summer, when they occupied summer cottages near their crop lands. They had five species of beans as their chief articles of diet, but they also raised corn, used the young shoots of many plants, and made syrup and preserves from the ripened fruit of the sahuaro and pitaya cacti. Considering the barren condition of their desert habitat, they possessed a remarkably varied and wholesome larder.

Those Indians were humane, and were among the

---

[19] See the legend, "The girl of Guevavi," for a biographical sketch of this great jesuit.

[20] These missions were turned over to the franciscans in 1768, following the expulsion of the jesuits from Spanish dominions.

most cheerful in America. In their religion, the spirit of good permeated everything; they did not recognize the existence of evil spirits. Their names for their supreme being were Big Brother and Spirit of Good. Their morality was high. Much of their legendary lore is beautiful, and none of it is degrading as is the lore of many of the native people of the southwest.

Following the establishment of the three missions named, Spanish settlers came into the Santa Cruz valley, and in 1751 a presidio was erected therein to protect missions and settlers from Apache raids. This, the presidio of Tubac, was during its existence the largest strictly military community on the whole frontier of New Spain.

However, the Apaches continued to harass the Arizona settlements until the year 1760, when Juan Bautista de Anza, representing the third generation of empire-builders in his genealogical line, was placed in command at Tubac. He pursued the same course that we observed him pursuing later in New Mexico. He made the Papagos, Yumas, and Pimas his allies against the Apaches, and speedily convinced the latter that raids were not profitable. He then put his soldiers to work at farming and created a beautiful oasis around Tubac, wherein many varieties of fruits and vegetables, as well as trees and flowers, were grown under irrigation.

In 1777, when Anza was transferred to the governorship of New Mexico, the Tubac presidio was abandoned and a new one established in its stead at Tucson.

In 1780 two combined missions and presidios were placed on the Colorado river, just below the junction of the Gila, to serve in part as way-stations on an overland route to California which Anza had opened up in 1774, and over which he had led a large consignment of colonists in the following year.[21] But the soldiers and settlers sent to those two establishments mistreated the Yuma Indians, and as a result they were completely wiped out of existence in 1781 and all the buildings burned by the Indians. No attempt was made to re-establish these posts and the overland route to California, of which Kino had dreamed nearly a century before, was permanently abandoned.

By the year 1800 the Santa Cruz valley was well filled with settlements, but the withdrawal of the Spanish garrison from Tucson in 1822 left the way open again to Apache raids, and as a result the valley soon was emptied of its colonists. The missions were abandoned in 1824, and when the United States took possession of Arizona in 1846 a small Mexican garrison, cooped up in the walled town of Tucson, was all that remained of the old glory of the Santa Cruz valley.

In 1856 Charles D. Poston brought 300 men, mostly miners and mining engineers, from Texas into Arizona. They occupied the old Tubac presidio, which then was still in good repair except that doors and windows were missing. These men varied their mining activities by replanting some of the old gardens and fields, and for a few years Tubac was a famous way-station on our southern overland route to California. Mexican settlers at the same time reoccupied the Santa Cruz valley. But when in 1861 the United States troops were withdrawn from that territory, even Poston's seasoned indian fighters were compelled to retreat before the Apaches. Arizona was not thereafter occupied by white settlers

21 See the sequel to "Dorotea's roses."

until the United States, after ten years' warfare and an expenditure of forty million dollars, had subdued those Ishmaels of the desert and herded them into reservations.

The old mission of the Angels of Guevavi has disappeared except for a few fragments of wall located nine miles east of Nogales, Arizona; and the Tumacacori, although a national monument, is now hopelessly in ruins. The San Xavier, however, was carefully cared for by the Papagos after its enforced abandonment, and early in this century it was repaired and restored under the direction of Bishop Granjon. It remains the finest example of mission architecture on this continent, but looks startlingly out of place in its desert setting. The famous old Tubac presidio has nearly all disappeared, although the ruins of the church, barracks, and main presidio building still were to be seen on the occasion of our last visit in 1908.

CALIFORNIA

California first was seen in 1542 by the maritime explorer, Rodriguez Cabrillo, whose ships reached latitude 42° 42' on the coast. Next came the English pirate, Francis Drake, who, sailing the Pacific in 1579 for the express purpose of "plundering and destroying Spanish ships and cities," [22] spent one month in a small bay just north of the Golden Gate. Drake took possession of the territory for England, naming it New Albion.

Drake's action caused consternation in the official

[22] Spain and England were not then at war, but according to Drake his piratical expedition had been instigated by Queen Elizabeth. Other English buccaneers, such as Frobisher, Cavendish, and Morgan, ravaged Spanish settlements and destroyed Spanish commerce, apparently with the connivance of their government.

circles of Mexico, and after storms and strong head winds had beaten back several expeditions, Sebastian Vizcaino in 1602 made a successful voyage up the coast, discovering and naming San Diego Bay and Monterey Bay – both missed by Cabrillo and Drake because of fogs and storms.

Various untoward circumstances, however, prevented the occupation of California (or California Alta as it then was called) for more than one and one-half centuries thereafter. That province was, in fact, nearly inaccessible from Mexico. Great stretches of waterless desert practically barred overland approach, and it was not until 1774 that a route circumventing these barriers was found. Also, the high head (north) winds prevailing off the coast of Lower California made the sea approach extremely hazardous at best, and vessels were lost time and again in these waters.

But when in the 1760's the English showed signs of activity on the Pacific coast, José de Galvez was sent from Spain as visitador-general, and one of his several commissions was to occupy and hold California Alta. He was the right man for the enterprise, and in 1769 a combined land and sea expedition (the land contingent coming up the peninsula from La Paz) arrived at San Diego Bay and there established a presidio and the mission of San Diego de Acalá – destined to grow into the present city of San Diego.

This post, however, was all but abandoned the following year, but with the timely arrival of additional supplies the settlement was put on a solid foundation. Another presidio and mission were erected on Monterey Bay in 1770 – the presidio of Monterey and the mission of San Carlos Borromeo.

The two missions named, as well as several later ones, were founded by Fray Junipero Serra, the first *padre presidente* of the California mission field and one of the outstanding figures in early California history, although we can not rank him as high as the great jesuit, Eusebio Kino, of Arizona and Sonora.

In the year of our national independence San Francisco was founded by Anza of Arizona, who had conducted an expedition of colonists overland from Sonora into California.[23]

By the end of the eighteenth century Spain had eighteen thriving missions strung along the coastal district from San Diego to San Francisco, but only three civilian towns – San José, Branciforte, and Los Angeles – had been founded, and the second of these was short-lived. Most of the urban population was clustered about the presidios of San Diego, Monterey, and San Francisco, and later, Santa Barbara.

Little trouble was had at any time with the Indians of the coastal belt. Those from the interior, however, said to be more vigorous, warlike, and intelligent than the coastal tribes, occasionally attacked the missions and settlements, but never with any very serious consequences.

Prudent writers do not attempt to classify the California Indians, other than to remark that they comprised more than twenty linguistic families. Ridpath declared that they lacked courage and intelligence, that they were indolent (in which characteristic they were not unique) and that their social condition was degraded.

[23] The actual founding of San Francisco was by Anza's second in command, Joaquin Moraga.

They were semi-sedentary and their diet, according to Professor C. E. Chapman, consisted of "nearly everything that teeth could bite." The women did all the work. The men did the fighting, but they were sorry warriors, and their battles never were sanguinary. They practiced no agriculture, made no pottery, had no occupations other than the perpetual one of hunting fleas. Their ideas of morality were hazy, inconsistent, and of a low order. They had no organized religion, and evil spirits, the chief of which was Puy, predominated.

Such was the material which the missionary padres proposed to transform, and did transform into useful artisans and farmers.

Additional exploring was done up the coast during the last quarter of the eighteenth century, and one Spanish ship mapped the coast up to latitude 54° 40'. Since our later claim to the Pacific coast was in part based upon Spain's claim, this gave rise to the campaign cry of 1844 – "Fifty-four forty or fight!"

The year 1790, however, marked the end of the northward expansion of Spain's colonial empire. In 1789 some English ships had been seized at Nootka Sound (Vancouver Island) and as a result England and Spain nearly came to blows. But in their treaty, the following year, it was provided that England should hold the territory southward to Puget Sound and Spain that northward to the present northern limits of California. The region in between was to belong to whichever nation occupied it first.

The fertile interior valleys of California never were occupied, all settlements being in the narrow coastal belt. Monterey, the largest town, was the capital and residence of the governor.

The interval from 1790 to 1820 is known as the romantic period of California history. The people were tolerably comfortable, the missions provided most of the manufactured goods needed, and the province was fortunately shut off by desert and sea from the distractions of the outside world. The people were ignorant and consequently, happy. Some enlivenment was provided at times by yankee smugglers and trading ships, and the capture of Monterey by the pirate Bouchard in 1818 furnished excitement for a time.

The revolution in Mexico was hardly felt in faraway California, although the pure-blood Spanish people there, being mostly royalists, objected mildly to the change of flags and some of them left the province. A few petty revolts against Mexico's rule were indulged in during the quarter-century 1822 to 1847, but none of these was formidable, though doubtless serious enough to the people at the time.

As a result of our war with Mexico, California was ceded to the United States and so, in the words of Chapman, "the work of Galvez and Bucareli, worthily carried on by the Spanish Californians, reached its logical conclusion." Here, as in New Mexico, it appears that a majority of the Spanish people made no objection to the change of flags.

Excepting New Mexico, California possesses more monuments of the Spanish period than any other state, although few of the buildings antedate the nineteenth century. Several of the missions have disappeared and others are in ruins, but there are a few that remain tolerably well preserved. Among the most interesting ones are the San Luis Rey, the San Gabriel, the San Fernando, the Santa Barbara, the San Buenaventura, and the Santa Inés. In Monterey is the old presidio chapel and two or three interesting colonial homes, all more or less intimately associated with the legendary lore of the state.

The Missions

Since the missions occupy such an important place in both the history and the legendary lore of the Spanish colonial period, a brief further mention of them may appropriately be made.

It being Spain's object to transform the Indian into an economic asset, the religious aspect of the missions was, in the eyes of the secular authorities, of less importance than the industrial especially as regards those of California and Texas.

Each mission was in charge of a *padre superior* and under him was the *mayor-domo* – usually a Spaniard or mestizo,[24] but sometimes an Indian – having general supervision of the industrial work of the mission. Under the *mayor-domo* were the various overseers, having immediate direction of the different industrial activities.

Exercising supervision over all the missions in any one field was the *padre presidente,* who usually was a man having a record of long and successful experience in missionary work.

The career of the missions was ended by secularization. Spain in 1813 ordered the transfer to the secular authorities of such missions as had been in existence ten years or more, in order that the friars might be

---

[24] The Spanish word mestizo really means one whose blood is half Spanish and half native, but we use it to mean any one of mixed Spanish and indian blood. Some of the leading men of the Spanish frontier – e.g., Juan de Oñate, the founder of New Mexico – were of mixed blood.

moved to new fields. This order was not enforced in
the frontier provinces nor generally elsewhere. In 1833
the government of Mexico ordered the secularization
of all missions within its domains. Whatever this may
have meant in theory, or whatever may have been intended, in execution it amounted to the confiscation of
the mission property, the consequent dispersion of the
mission Indians, and the reduction of the mission itself
to the status of a parish church, or its abandonment
altogether.

In Texas, New Mexico, and Arizona this order was
hardly felt. The missions of Texas had been secularized
in 1794. In Arizona the missions had ceased to function
as such in 1824. In New Mexico the missions owned
no land and little other property. Only in California
was the order of secularization followed by serious
consequences. The missions there had been producing
most of the manufactured goods and foodstuffs used in
the province, and their seizure was a real economic
blow. Such of the padres as desired to remain as parish
priests were permitted to do so, but in 1840 the so-called
pious fund belonging to the California, Lower California, and Sonora missions was diverted to the state
treasury so that the priests were left without means of
support.[25]

In 1844 the California missions were advertised for
sale by the government of Mexico and by 1846 all
except the Santa Barbara had been disposed of. The

[25] The pious fund was a large fund accumulated by the jesuits for the
prosecution of their missionary work in Sonora and Lower California, was
transferred to the franciscans when the jesuits were expelled, and was used
by them for work in California Alta as well as in the other two provinces.
It amounted to over $2,000,000 and in 1840 was yielding an annual income
of about six per cent.

United States government, however, refused to recognize these sales as valid and the buildings reverted to the church.

Much has been written of the Spanish missionary padres, mostly highly eulogistic. However, we believe that Captain A. M. Potter strikes the right note: [26] "If we owe to departed heroes the duty of preserving their deeds from oblivion, we ought to feel as strongly that duty of defending their memory against the calumnious effect of false eulogy which in time might cause their real achievements to be doubted."

Many of the padres possessed talents that would have won them recognition in almost any field of human activity and nearly all of them were, for their day, educated men. Most of them were men of high character and of whole-hearted devotion to their work. Yet they were but men; some of them were unnecessarily harsh toward their Indians; there were some who, according to Bishop F. C. Kelley, never should have entered the priesthood. There were a few misfits, just as there are, and always have been, misfits in every vocation on earth.

With the exception of the jesuits in southern Arizona prior to 1767, all the missionaries in our southwest were franciscans.

Life in the Spanish Colonies

The Spanish people are social and gregarious by nature; hence there was little of that isolation that marked frontier life in the Anglo-american colonies. Everybody, even the farmers, preferred to live in town,

---

26 Potter's reference was to the heroes of the Alamo in Texas, but his statement applies with equal force to the missionary padres.

although a small town often was scattered over a good
deal of ground and the average villa contained fewer
than 500 Spaniards. The ranchos and haciendas were
somewhat isolated, although the ranchero and hacen-
dado lived somewhat after the manner of a feudal baron,
with a swarm of retainers comprising Spanish overseers and mestizos or indian laborers who themselves
often formed a small village.

The town, however, was the characteristic feature
of the Spanish colonies and since each town usually
had not only its farmers and traders, but its smiths,
leather-workers, weavers, masons, millers, etc., each
community, after becoming well established, was nearly
self-supporting. This, however, was not so much the
case in California where the colonists remained to the
end dependent to a considerable extent upon the missions for many of the necessities of life. Everywhere,
though, the colonists had a commendable capacity for
taking things in a leisurely way whenever there was
no urgent necessity for haste.

The colonial homes were built of burned brick,
adobe brick, or stone and were almost invariably of
one story, usually of no more than three or four rooms
and often of only two. The more pretentious residence
of from six to twelve rooms, however, was built in the
form of a hollow rectangle inclosing a little court or
patio which often was planted with flowers and shrubbery. The roofs were nearly flat except in California
where the prolonged winter rains made a pitched roof
necessary. The bright tile roofs of the California pioneers survive to this day as a feature of the modern
architecture of that state, even as the moorish pueblo
style used in New Mexico three centuries ago is used

today for even the most pretentious public and private buildings there.

The dwellings of the colonists usually surrounded a central plaza of two to four acres, wherein the people gathered for gossip, amusement, and music on summer evenings and holidays. They were fond of music and every community of any size had a band or orchestra of some sort, sometimes half a dozen of them, mostly of stringed instruments. Some of the missions even had bands; the San Luis Rey had an indian band of 40 pieces, while the Santa Clara had a uniformed indian orchestra.[27]

The Spanish colonists also were fond of flowers, dress, dancing, and conversation, and the men, we regret to add, enjoyed games of chance. Imported silks, satins, and velvets were known from the very start; life would have been intolerable without these luxuries, although the absence of chinaware and stoves was viewed with entire complacency. But it is not to be assumed that the people as a whole were frivolous or devoted to superficiality. The first colonists sent to Branciforte, San José, and Los Angeles in California were a ne'er-do-well, unpromising sort, but the exigencies of frontier life soon eliminated the worst of them and regenerated those who were worth saving.[28] Aside from these, as nearly as we can learn, the Spanish who settled in our southwest seem to have been of good

[27] The Frenchman, Duhaut-Cilly, visiting the Santa Clara mission in 1827, was astonished to hear very creditable renditions of Les Marseillaise and Vive le roi played in his honor, although, since France then was not a monarchy, the latter air was hardly appropriate.

[28] During the later years of Spanish rule, many of the submerged class were sent from Mexico to California, where most of them became good citizens. Chapman suggests that probably these unfortunates never had a chance before.

quality. The founders of Santa Fe and Albuquerque counted many old and stable Spanish names and the colonists who established San Antonio, Texas, were of the soundest class, even though they were accused of looking down upon later comers and of refusing to associate with the families of the soldiers at Bexar presidio.

The towns of each province were connected by trails and from the settled districts of Texas, New Mexico, and Arizona roads led down through Mexico to Mexico City, with branches to seaports on both coasts. California alone had no feasible overland trail to Mexico, although the road that connected the settlements of that province ran on down the peninsula of Lower California to La Paz, whence it was a short voyage across the gulf to the mainland. Until the year 1810 a supply ship made the voyage from San Blas to California each year and other ships of various nations occasionally touched at San Diego, Santa Barbara, Monterey, and San Francisco. The Manila Galeón, which made an annual voyage from Acapulco to the Orient and back, was supposed to stop at Monterey on each return voyage but it rarely did so.

The New Mexicans, although the most nearly isolated of all, had two great diversions each year. These were fairs, one held at Taos in midsummer, and the other at Chihuahua, Mexico, in january. It has been claimed that half the population of the province attended each of these. This may have been true a few times, but we doubt that it was true as a general thing.

To the Taos fair came Indians of many tribes to trade their wares, mostly hides and furs, for the manufactured goods of the Spaniards, while at Chihuahua merchants from Vera Cruz, Mexico City, Pueblo, Acapulco, and even from Spain, had their goods on display. Both scenes must have been worthy of perpetuation upon canvas but the artist was wanting.

The Texas colonists attended the Chihuahua fair, more or less, and those of Arizona and Sonora patronized the fairs at Guaymas. A big fair was held at Acapulco each year, after the arrival of the Manila Galeón, and merchants came from as far as Peru to buy. The largest fair of all – that at Jalapa – was too remote to be more than sparingly visited by the people of the frontier provinces.

For conveying freight on land, ox-teams and pack-mules were used. There were plenty of horses but these were used mainly for mounts. In the frontier provinces there were few carriages outside of San Antonio, Santa Fe, and Monterey, and nearly everybody rode horseback, both men and women being skilled equestrians. Visitors to the provinces commented upon the fact that the entire population seemed to be mounted.

The leading occupation was stock-raising and the per capita number of cattle and sheep often ran into the hundreds. In California, when shipping facilities were wanting, great numbers of cattle were slaughtered to prevent over-stocking, while in New Mexico large herds of sheep were driven to market in Mexico over the famous old trail of the conquistadores.

Some farming was done but rarely was there any considerable surplus of farm crops. Corn, beans, wheat, fruit, and vegetables were the staple crops, nor must we forget wine-grapes, from which several celebrated brands of wine and brandy were made. Indians were largely employed as farm laborers and herdsmen.

It was a poor household that did not have at least one servant. Most of the actual servants were Indians who had been captured from hostile or gentile tribes. Doubtless many of them were not fairly treated, but as a rule they received as much consideration as usually is accorded servants by the dominant race.

Slavery was imposed upon the Indian only as a punishment for crime, but the Spanish had nearly as long a list of crimes as had our New England forefathers. In addition, rebellion on the part of Indians who had taken the oath of allegiance to the crown of Spain was considered a crime. Captured rebels, therefore, often were sentenced to slavery, but nearly always for limited terms, and only really serious offenses drew sentences of ten years or more.

While the oppression or enslavement of christianized natives except as a punishment for crime was absolutely forbidden by royal decree, yet their condition in some districts was hardly better than that of serfs. The system of *repartimiento,* authorized by the crown, permitted the Spaniards to draft not to exceed three per cent of the Indians of any village for labor on a share basis, when their labor was needed; but at times, as during harvests, nearly the entire available supply of natives was drafted, and their employers were the judges as to what should be their share.

The proportion of mestizos among the colonists who came up from Mexico naturally increased progressively through the colonial period. The pioneers who occupied New Mexico early in the seventeenth century were nearly all Spaniards, while most of those who came into California nearly two centuries later were of mixed blood.

Education was in the hands of the priests almost exclusively, and they taught reading, writing, and elementary arithmetic, along with the catechism. The priests probably were more liberally educated than were the contemporary schoolmasters of New England, but in the opinion of many people they overemphasized religious instruction.

During the first quarter of the nineteenth century Spain lost nearly all her vast colonial empire. The causes appear in detail upon the pages of history, and so need be stated but briefly here.

Straitened by the drains her overseas colonies made upon her resources, and further impoverished by the European wars of the eighteenth century climaxed by the Napoleonic wars, Spain declined to the point where she no longer was able to defend her frontiers or, in fact, any part of her New World possessions. Her scheme of conquest involved not only the enforced civilization of the natives within the regions occupied, but the protection of them, as well as the Spanish colonists, from the onslaughts of the gentile tribes that were without the pale. This necessitated the presence of military forces on all her frontiers, and a strong and efficient military organization was expensive.

We find a parallel between Spain in America and England in India. Spain was trying to civilize the Indians and improve their condition against their wishes. She educated them and taught them the use of European weapons and European military strategy, and then when the time was opportune they turned this training against their teacher.[29]

---

[29] The first revolt in 1810 consisted mostly of Indians led by a mestizo priest named Hidalgo and, according to Bishop F. C. Kelley, it was a revolt against Napoleon rather than against Spain.

After Mexico won her independence, her government ordered the expulsion or deportation of all Spaniards, but in the enforcement of this decree those who would take the oath of allegiance to Mexico were allowed to remain. Most of them left.

OUR HERITAGE FROM SPAIN

We have a legacy from Spain probably greater than that from all other nations combined excepting England. The colonial French and Dutch are given much more attention in our histories than are the Spanish, yet in comparison with the last, the influence of the other two is negligible.

There are many Spaniards in our southwest and they are of the most stable, intelligent, and progressive element of southwestern society. They always have been so and the history of the southwest under the United States flag, as well as under the standard of Castile and Aragon, is enriched with the names of Spanish patriots and empire-builders.

Spain is indelibly impressed upon this region. Ten states bear Spanish names; even far-away Oregon received its name from the wild marjoram (Spanish *orégano*) that abounds in that state. Most of the mountains and all the streams worth mentioning in the southwest bear Spanish names, most of the canyons and hills echo the musical tongue of Old Castile, and the popular names of the plants and animals of this region are either Spanish or Hispanized indian.

Many words of everyday use in the United States are Spanish or of Spanish origin. Among the hundreds of such, we mention here just a few that occur to us as we write: ranch, coffee, cafeteria, mosquito, lagoon, frontier, renegade, guerilla, creole, captain, filibuster, banana, jalap, tomato, alligator, canoe, cocoa, etc., not to mention such slang words as palaver, hoosegow, pickaninny, loco, pooch, etc.

Such tropical and subtropical fruits as oranges, lemons, figs, dates, avocados, and grapes were introduced into our southwest by the Spanish, and some of their introductions still are preferred to the later productions of the modern horticulturists. They also introduced several temperate-zone food plants that had become adapted to dry climates on the semi-arid plateaus of Spain. Our morning cup of cocoa is another gift from the colonial Spaniard.

But the popular assumption that such dishes as tamales, frijoles, tortillas, and enchiladas are Spanish is incorrect. These highly-flavored concoctions are strictly indian dishes.

The predominant styles of architecture in New Mexico, Arizona, and California are of Spanish inspiration. In the first-named state, Spanish colonial architecture predominates today even in such structures as hotels, railway depots, and federal buildings and is peculiarly in harmony with the aspect of nature in this region.

Much of the Spanish jurisprudence has been incorporated into the constitutions and statutes of the southwestern states to the extent that today no student of law in this country can be said to have completed his course of study until he has mastered Spanish-american law. The social code, too, of the southwest reflects the Spanish influence, which also is clearly seen in the art and literature of the region.

Finally, the capacity of the southwestern people for being leisurely and for enjoying their leisure is a direct inheritance from the Spaniards who, although as capable as any people on earth of acting with celerity and dispatch, never were in a hurry unless the circumstances actually demanded haste. The Spaniard believed that life is granted us to enjoy and he held that haste and happiness are incompatible.

New Mexico Legends

New Mexico Legends

In view of New Mexico's three centuries of stirring and variegated colonial history, one would expect to find a much greater range in its legendary lore than actually exists.

It has many depressing stories of indian raids and ambushes, probably true, but much alike and all tragic.

The state also possesses many buried-treasure legends; these, all built upon the same basic plot, are entirely fiction, since they are based upon the wholly fictitious traditions of wealth obtained from the gran quivira region and cached there or elsewhere.

Then there are innumerable little household legends that have sprung up in the Mexican communities of the state during the last 100 years. While some of these are charming, they hardly can be included as a part of the lore of the Spanish period.

Our readers are offered only the two most dramatic of the legends of indian attacks. Of the treasure legends none were considered worthy of the reader's attention.

In addition to the legends that follow, there are several others that deserve mention: "The town of the broken promise," "Fray Padilla," "The massacre at Fernandez de Taos," "Bandini," "Teresa Vallejo," "Perdido," "Pablo the jester," and the "Miracle of San Felipe." These are our titles. The first named one has appeared in print, in some detail, under the title "The Comanche's revenge." The others, so far as we

know, never have appeared in print except in a skele-
tonized form.

La Jornada del Muerte

Between the Rio Grande and the San Andreas mountains in southern New Mexico there is a desert region, wherein for a distance of 90 miles north and south, and about 30 miles east and west, there is but one source of water – a small spring which lies six miles off the trail in the mountains.

West of the river the country is too broken to permit of travel parallel to the stream, while on the east side the Fra Cristobal and Sierra Caballo ranges crowd right down to the water's edge. Thus it is necessary for travelers to depart from the river and pass between these mountains and the gaunt ridge of the San Andreas, 30 miles to the east. This 90 mile stretch of desolation has come to be known as *la jornada del muerto* (the journey of the dead man, literally translated) but we are informed by Spanish-americans of New Mexico that its original name was *la jornada del muerte* (the journey of death) and this name we have adopted. We also have heard it referred to as *la via del muerte* (the way of death) and Anza in 1779 called it *el camino del muerto*.

A century ago the road through that desert was mile-posted with graves. Richardson, passing through on the mail stage in 1859, wrote, "At midnight we entered the *jornada del muerto*. This desert, 90 miles long, contains no water except a single spring several miles from the road. Many travelers have perished of thirst here,

and upon the ground bleach the bones of scores of
animals. But two days before us, the mail party discovered two corpses by the roadside."

It is from one of the episodes of the following legend
that this desert is said to have received its gruesome
name. This is one of the oldest legends, belonging to
the white race, within the limits of the United
States. – C.H.

It seemed that all the Spanish population of Nueva
Galicia, and many of the Indians, too, were gathered
at Compostela on that morning in may, 1540, when
Francisco Vasquez de Coronado was to start northward
on his search for the Golden Cities of Cibola.

For a year all Mexico had been agog with excitement,
for Marcos de Niza had declared that he had gazed
with his own eyes upon one of those cities and had seen
the rays of the setting sun burnishing its golden walls
and battlements.

Nearly a year had been spent in organizing and
equipping the expedition. And now, on the morn of
its departure, Compostela presented a gala aspect.
Helmeted and in their saddles, the colors of their wives
and sweethearts floating from the points of their lances
or fluttering from their helmets, were 300 of the young
hidalgos of New Spain. Many of them were wild and
unruly blades whom viceroy Mendoza, a lover of peace,
had induced to join the expedition in order to get rid
of them.

At the head of the slowly-forming column Coronado
in his golden armor sat motionless as an equestrian
statue, waiting for stragglers to get into line; Coronado,
young, handsome, brilliant, whom Mendoza through

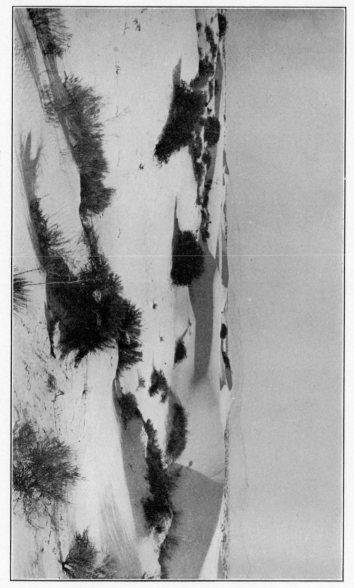

THE WHITE SANDS OF LA JORNADA DEL MUERTE

envy had appointed head of this expedition, foreseeing
that it would end in disaster.

A number of brown-robed brothers of the order of
friars minor stood about in farewell conversation with
the four priests of their order who were to accompany
the expedition, while to the rear lolled at ease 800 wiry,
brown Indians; tireless fellows who could travel as
far in a day as a horse. Friends and relatives of the
departing men were on every hand and from the throng
arose an incessant chatter of animated conversation.

To one side, separated from the general crowd, stood
the brown-haired Juan de Escobar, his bridle over his
arm, and beside him was Maria, his bride of less than
three months. The trumpets sounded "fall in!" and
Escobar enfolded his wife in a final embrace.

"A Dios, now, *querida mía,"* he whispered to her.
"I soon will return, bringing you great riches from the
mines of Cibola. The good God watch over and guard
thee, my love!"

"And God guard you, *querido mío,"* answered Maria,
tremulously, "Each day I shall pray long to the *Santissima Maria* for you."

With a last kiss, Escobar swung into his saddle and
hurried to his place in the column that, with silken
banners unfurled and lances at rest, prepared to move.

Then Coronado at the head of the column flashed his
sword aloft and cried, *"Dios y Santiago! Quien vivera,
vera!"* (God and Saint James! He who lives, shall see!)
and the cry was echoed from every hand. In an uproar
of shouts and farewells the column set itself in motion.
After the mounted cavaliers on their gaily-caparisoned
horses came the supply train, and then the long queue
of silent, half-naked Indians.

Maria, rising light as a bird to her saddle, sat and waited, hoping for a final glimpse of her husband with her colors — silver and blue — floating from his helmet. Doubtless her wish was carried to Escobar, for as the breeze broke the dust pall and momentarily revealed him to her, he turned in his saddle and waved a final farewell.

Day by day the expedition moved northward, guided by Marcos de Niza, excitement rising higher and higher as the mountain valleys and mesas were left behind. When on a day in july Marcos volunteered the information that the first of the wonderful cities would be reached before nightfall, discipline was thrown to the winds. The men hurried forward as rapidly as the nature of the country would permit, the naked canyons ringing with their songs and their cries of *quien vivera!*

Finally, from the crest of a low ridge Hawikuh, the largest of the Cities of Cibola, lay before them. But their eager anticipation was on the instant changed to chagrin and rage. The enchanted city was nothing but an indian village of stone and adobe! And across the trail its people had drawn their line of sacred meal, forbidding the white strangers entry into their town.

But Coronado's men, disregarding this warning, pushed on into the village where they were at once attacked. The crude weapons of the natives were no match for the swords and lances of the Spaniards and presently the warriors fled and the old men came out and sued for peace.

Great now was the anger against the luckless Marcos, and only the restraining hand of Coronado prevented harm to him. He was ordered to depart forthwith for Mexico.

Each of the remaining towns of the Zuñis now was visited, but all were alike. There was no gold and the natives were unable to tell the Spaniards where any mines were to be found. But they told Coronado of a group of seven other cities that lay to the northwest, so he, going into camp at Hawikuh, dispatched a small expedition in that direction. In this detail was Escobar. Before leaving he had dispatched a letter to Maria by an indian courier, informing her of his bitter disappointment, but assuring her that the discovery of gold mines was only delayed.

While this expedition under Captain Cardenas visited the seven ancient cities of the Moqui Indians and beheld that matchless miracle of nature, the Grand Canyon of the Colorado, it found no gold or silver and, after a journey of 600 miles, arrived again at Hawikuh.

Coronado's little army next moved eastward to the Rio Grande, in the heart of the pueblo country, and went into quarters at the pueblo of Tiguex.

This story has nothing to do [30] with Coronado's subsequent journey through Texas, Oklahoma, and into eastern Kansas in search of the kingdom of Quivira. But while encamped at Tiguex, the entire pueblo region was explored by detachments of his army. One detail of some 20 men was sent down the Rio Grande.

In this squad was Escobar. After proceeding for 80 miles down the west side of the river, the men crossed to the east side, where the going was easier. Here a range of mountains, low at first but gradually becoming higher and more precipitous, crept between the men and the river and shut them off from water.

---

[30] Something more of Coronado's expedition will be found in the legend of "The gran quivira."

On the second night after crossing the Rio Grande, Escobar's horse, with two others, disappeared. Their tracks were found the next morning, leading off to the southeast. The owners of the strayed mounts were dispatched to find their horses, with instructions to rejoin the company farther south.

The squad then moved on, with the intention of making camp at the first water encountered and there awaiting the three men. But no water was found. They had but a very small supply with them and it was necessary that they go on until they had located a stream or spring. For two days, then three, they marched southward. On the evening of the third day, following up an arroyo, they found a tiny, spring-fed stream.

Here, after a consultation, the men decided to turn back. It was necessary to rescue the three missing men if possible.

But on the return journey the missing companions were sought fruitlessly, because the wind had obliterated any tracks they might have left. Finally, conceding them lost, the company moved on and rejoined the main body at Tiguex, where the loss was reported to Coronado.

Meanwhile, in the desert of dead men, the sun beat in smothering waves upon the white sands, the stark rocks, the black wastes of volcanic obsidian. Moving slowly through the heat-shimmer was the emaciated form of a man, clad in rags, his head bowed upon his chest. In his right hand he held a sword, the point of which had been broken off, and he was using this blade as a cane to steady his footsteps. Occasionally he stopped and stared with bloodshot eyes, as though trying to fix his gaze on some distant object. Far ahead of him stood a lone bisnaga cactus, like the dark stump of some prehistoric column, and with a desperate persistence the man guided his feet toward it.

Two days before he had seen the first of his companions sink down and, unable to rise or speak, by feeble gestures implore the others to abandon him and seek to save themselves.

For another day the two survivors had fought the relentless heat, seeking a gap in the gaunt mountain wall that shut them away from water. Now this man had just left the lifeless body of his remaining companion unburied on the hot sands.

On finally reaching the giant cactus, he stopped and, holding his sword unsteadily in both hands, hacked into the spongy column and sucked greedily at its juices. He hacked again, and again glued his mouth to the watery pulp. Twice more he slashed into the plant and quenched his burning thirst with its insipid but life-giving sap.

He lay down in the shadow of a large rock for the remainder of the day. With the setting of the sun and the attendant great fall in temperature, he rose weakly, hacked and sucked anew at the cactus, then painfully resumed his journey.

In Mexico City, Maria had not heard from Escobar since his arrival at Tiguex. From there he had dispatched his second letter to her, along with Coronado's report to the viceroy, announcing his intention to continue to the end and bidding her not to lose hope.

A slow year dragged by, and another winter. Then the despondent Maria was electrified by the news that Coronado's expedition had been sighted on the Sonora river, journeying homeward.

Maria made hasty preparations to go to Compostela to meet Escobar. Accompanied by two servants, she set out the next day on the 600 mile journey. She reached Compostela thirteen days later, just as the advance stragglers of Coronado's army were arriving. Encountering one of Escobar's fellow-officers, she made eager inquiry as to his whereabouts. This officer knew of Escobar's fate, but he took refuge in a falsehood.

"Señora," he informed her, "Don Escobar formed one of a party of 20 that started homeward down the Rio del Norte as the shorter route to Mexico City. Unless he met with some unforeseen delay, he should be in Mexico City by this time."

Maria, disappointed but rejoicing nevertheless, hurried back along the road to the capital, expecting that her husband, if he had arrived, would ride to meet her.

But day after day passed without her encountering any one except chance travelers. Upon finally reaching her home she abandoned her horse to her servants and ran into the patio, where her native maid-servant met her with an impassive countenance.

"Don Juan –," began Maria, breathlessly.

"The Señor Escobar has not come, Señora," replied the servant.

"Not here! Not returned?" gasped Maria, stumbling blindly. The servant caught her and placed her in a seat.

"My husband has not come back?" asked Maria, staring into the Indian's face.

"Doubtless the Señor Escobar returned," lied the servant, sympathetically, "and learning that you were gone, went to the house of your parents, thinking to find you there."

"I must go there," whispered Maria, rising quickly.

"I must know! Surely," her voice rising to a scream, "surely God would not be so cruel to me!"

A month had elapsed since the return of Coronado's expedition and it had ceased to be a subject for daily gossip. Coronado, once the idol of the aristocracy of New Spain, broken in health and humbled by viceroy Mendoza, was forgotten.

Maria wanted only seclusion. Passersby occasionally glimpsed her in the little flower-grown patio of her home, but she never passed beyond its portals. It now had become her sanctuary.

One morning her faithful Tezcucan servant, with the stolid persistence of the Indian, had insisted that she come out of the house into the fresh air and cheering sunlight of the patio, and she had listlessly obeyed. With her hands folded loosely in her lap, the young woman became oblivious of everything about her, and unconscious of the passage of time.

A sudden scream from her servant startled her.

"Mi Dios!" shrieked the Indian. "It is Don Juan!"

Maria leaped to her feet and whirled about. She saw, approaching through the arched passageway, the emaciated face and figure of a brown-haired man. She rushed to him and flung herself into his arms.

Finally Maria, looking up with wet eyes, whispered, "Oh, *caro mio! Mi esposo!* They told me that you had died! that you had died!"

"Does a man die, O beloved," asked Juan, huskily, "when he knows that a friend like you awaits him?"

At length Juan led her to the seat she had abandoned. They sat long silent. Then Juan spoke of his fight for life.

"That awful desert," he said, slowly, "I shall dream

of it always. Four days in that death trap killed both my companions. I wandered through it for nine days. Ah, but it was a *jornada del muerte!* Quite by accident I found a small spring and there I fell in with some Indians who fed me and took me to their camp. When my health was restored, they would not let me go. For more than a year – it seemed to me an eternity – they kept me with them. Finally I escaped."

Then Juan's eyes became troubled. "But I have failed," he said, shamefacedly. "I found no gold. I found nothing but suffering. I have returned to you shamed and defeated."

"Ah, *esposo,*" interrupted Maria, happily, "but it is I who have a treasure for you! Come with me."

She led the wondering man into the house, and there, in a crib, lay a baby of eighteen months, with Juan's chestnut hair and violet eyes. It greeted its mother with a chuckle, then regarded its father appraisingly. Juan sank to his knees beside the crib and Maria knelt beside him.

"Ah, but it is true," he said, at last, as though speaking to himself, "it is the woman who brings us the greatest treasures of the world." He turned Maria's face to him. "Had I brought you all the wealth of the kingdom of Quivira, *querida mía,*" he continued, "yet it had been tawdry beside your gift."

Another version of this legend states that the company of men who went down the Rio Grande was a band of disgruntled men who, separating themselves from Coronado, took that route homeward in 1542 and after losing Escobar and two others in the desert, continued on to Mexico City, arriving there well ahead of

Coronado. This story, however, has no historical support, while there is documentary record of the detachment that descended the Rio Grande in the late summer of 1540. Consequently, we have accepted the version that is in part supported by the evidence.

Maria's brother, Pedro, is one of the characters in the version we have related, but he is a mere figurehead, playing no part in the story itself; hence, for brevity, we have left him out. – C.H.

El Camino del Padre

After their crushing defeat by Zaldivar in 1598, the humbled Acoma Indians abandoned their village and betook themselves to the mountains. Not until 1625, when a new generation had arisen, did they come back to their desolated *penol* and doggedly set about rebuilding their ruined pueblo.

In that year came also from Spain the able Fray Alonso Benavides, commissioned to rejuvenate and extend the mission field of New Mexico. As a result of his efforts, all the indian pueblos of the province, except only Acoma, were brought under the spiritual domination of the church. Acoma, isolated, embittered, brooding, held hostilely aloof.

At last, in 1629 Fray Juan Ramirez, departing from Santa Fe against the advice of his friends, reached Acoma and accomplished the impossible. – C.H.

Governor Zotylo and Fray Juan Ramirez sat before a deeply-recessed window of the *palacio*. "I warn you, Padre Juan," expostulated the governor, "that it is sheer folly for you to approach the people on the rock of Acoma without an armed guard!"

Father Juan remained silent.

"You understand, Padre," continued the official, "that your task of reducing the Acomians will be a most perilous one? A task which, if you undertake alone, will result only in your throwing away your life?" The governor seemed puzzled by the priest's silence and apparent indifference. But now Father Juan's face set in lines of determination.

"Señor Governor-general," he answered quietly, "my work has taken me into perilous ways before. And my life lies in the hands of God."

The governor leaned back in his chair. "For four years," he remarked, "your brothers, the religious, and we officials have been trying to prevail upon the Acomians to make their peace with us and accept our religion and our protection. It is impossible! Our indian messengers tell us that the Acomians keep their piles of stones at the top of their cliff ever ready for – for our heads! A stone weighing one *arroba,* Padre, would end your life's work for all time!"

The governor chuckled at his grim joke. Then,

"Vincente Zaldivar gave them a lesson they have not forgotten," he went on. "Ah, but that was a most excellent piece of work, Padre! But it will make your position in their pueblo – if, indeed, they permit you to reach it – the more precarious. A sufficient guard of soldiers would not serve to pacify those people, but it would afford you protection. I urge you to reconsider . . ."

"I can manage better alone, Señor."

"A martyr's death, Padre Juan . . ."

"Is my privilege, Señor Governor-general."

The governor shrugged resignedly, the two arose and went out into the long veranda of the *palacio* and stood gazing over the sun-bathed plaza. Father Juan felt that he had used good judgment in refusing a guard of soldiers. He had his own plan for overcoming the enmity of the Acomians and now that the time

for his departure was drawing near, he was eager to
see the gigantic rock and its proud inhabitants whom
he desired to bring into the fold of the church.

Seeing that Padre Juan was about to start on his
long tramp to the "sky-dwelling" Acomians, his friends
and well-wishers – Spaniards, mestizos, and Indians –
flocked to the scene to bid him farewell. The governor
told him goodbye, adding,

"You will find the Indians along the way quite
friendly. It is only the people on the cliff whom you
need to fear. If they should learn of your intentions,
they might waylay you along the trail."

Then, accompanied by one of his brother priests,
Father Juan departed. At the outskirts of the settlement
he turned and gazed back at the City of the Holy
Faith, surrounded by its gray hills, basking in the
spring sunshine. Then his companion turned back and
Father Juan resolutely turned his footsteps to the west.

On through the parched deserts, mesas, and gloomy
canyons, with the frolicking of prairie dogs, the sweep
of bird wings, or the silent floating of new-born clouds
his only diversion in many leagues of travel, Father
Juan made his way toward the great Rock of Acoma.
Shutting from his mind thoughts of the death that
might await him just over the crest of each hill or in
the rocky vastness of each canyon, he trudged on, studying the land and its untamed beauty or dreaming of
the time when his indian neophytes would work with
him in peace and unison.

Then came a cool night on the wind-swept mesas
west of the San José river, when he realized that his
journey was near its end and that before the falling of
another night the success or failure of his mission would

be determined. With his head pillowed on his arm, he tried to sleep for with the new day he would have to pit his wits and tact against the intolerance of hundreds of fierce savages.

After a short rest he again was on his way and at the break of dawn he saw in the distance the famed *penol* of Acoma, with its quaint town peeping just over the edge of the table-like summit.

As the morning light spread and uncovered the plains, the priest realized that he had been seen by the natives. Those on top the *penol* swarmed close to the edge and watched his movements with hand-shaded eyes; those who had started for the field, having been signaled, ran to the base of the cliff and ascended its steep pathways with astonishing ease and celerity.

For the first time since he set out, a sense of his utter isolation smote upon the priest. His schemes for meeting and pacifying the bloodthirsty savages were forgotten. But he did not falter. He walked bravely forward.

Father Juan reached the foot of the citadel of stone and sought a place to climb, paying no attention to the growing clamor from above. He examined the precipitous sides that rose 300 feet above his head. There were three trails up the rock, but by chance he fell upon the most difficult one – a devious pathway that in places was formed of shallow niches cut into the almost vertical sides of the broken cliff – and began to clmb. The brink, more than 300 feet above, was crowded with excited Indians, howling, screeching, gesticulating. Whenever the priest came clearly into their view, they let fly arrows at him. None of them struck his flesh, but occasionally one passed through

The Rock of Acoma

his robe, and once the sudden tug of an arrow striking the thick cloth nearly caused him to lose his footing. After a while the stone ladderway led him underneath an overhanging shelf of rock, screening him from the enemy, and there he paused to rest and to pray God for courage to face again the arrows and stones of the misguided pagans.

Starting on, he presently came once more into view of the natives, like a great insect clinging to the steep wall, and his reappearance was greeted by additional arrows and bounding stones.

On and on he climbed, more slowly now because the ascent was becoming increasingly difficult. The confusion at the top became more and more intense as the priest came nearer, and women and children joined the massed throng.

Looking up, Father Juan saw that the natives were hovering on the very edge of the precipice, and in their disorder were shoving each other back and forth. As he watched, one little girl who had squeezed her way to the front of the mob in order to get a good view of the strange intruder stood on the very brink. She leaned cautiously over to see the climber; then a sudden surge of the crowd toppled her over the edge and she hurtled downward through the air out of their sight.

Horrified dismay momentarily silenced the noisy chorus. Then a roar of vengeful howls followed the little girl's drop into space and the enraged natives began to hurl great stones down at the daring climber. Luckily, at that moment, he passed underneath another overhanging ledge and was hidden from the eyes of the Indians. There he left the trail for he had witnessed a thing that the natives could not see, the child had fallen no more than ten or twelve yards and had landed on the very ledge under which Father Juan now was picking his way.

He pulled himself over crag and treacherous crevice until, availing himself of every little foothold, he finally clambered up on the shelving rock where the child lay. He still was hidden from the eyes of the Acomians, but an ominous silence told him that, scarcely more than 30 feet over his head, the enemies were tensely awaiting his reappearance. The child had fallen into deep-drifted sand and, while stunned into temporary unconsciousness, she was unhurt. It was with a glad heart that Father Juan lifted the girl and made his way back to the stone ladder.

At that point the trail led off to the right, where it again became visible from the top. From there on it was an almost vertical ladderway whereon, if a man lost his footing, he would fall to the base of the mesa.

Foremost among the savages waiting with poised stones and with arrows fitted to their bowstrings was Hak-i-wah, the father of the little girl. A murderous light gleamed in his deep-set eyes. Father Juan, the innocent cause of the accident, need expect no mercy from this man.

Suddenly the priest appeared from behind the buttress of rock, and there came a wild howl of fury; simultaneously came a screamed command from Hak-i-wah for them to hold! Because the priest, laboriously making his way up the last stone ladder, carried in his right arm the little girl whom they had believed crushed and lifeless on the rocks below. She was alive and unhurt and clinging confidently to her rescuer!

Mute with amazement and awe, the Indians silently

fell back as Father Juan completed his climb and clambered over the brink of the cliff, setting the child safely on the ground. They regarded the girl as one who had returned from the dead, but her mother and Hak-i-wah seized her and, finding that she was uninjured, began excitedly to question her.

Father Juan realized that the whole success of his mission depended now on this child. She rose to the occasion and declared that from the time she felt herself falling until she woke in this stranger's arms, she knew nothing; and that he must have caught her as she fell, in spite of the the fact that he was some distance away at the time. She finished by declaring that this pale-faced intruder was one of the trues.

The occurrence was regarded as miraculous by the people for certainly, they agreed, only by the aid of the most powerful of gods could the strongest man catch a body falling from the cliff without himself being torn from his footing and carried down to his death. Added to that was the amazing fact that he must have reached out 30 or 40 feet to one side to catch the girl! The people ran to their dwellings to bring gifts of food and blankets to this superior being. Hak-i-wah, with humility, begged the priest to enter his home and eat of his food, as a proof that he bore no ill-will toward the man who had most desired to slay him. But Hak-i-wah was overruled by his fellows who held that, as the guest of the city and as one favored by the most powerful of the gods, the stranger could be properly entertained only in the home of the *cacique*.

So the Acomians received Father Juan as a good wizard, sent them by the chief of all gods, and they accepted the priest as their spiritual leader. He dwelt with them until his death in 1664 – 35 years – and during that time he transformed the Acomians from the fiercest of the Pueblo tribes into the gentlest and most civilized in the whole southwest. Under his direction these people built a great stone church covering an area greater than that of any cathedral in the United States today and, in addition, a cemetery 200 feet square with walls 45 feet high on its lower boundary, carrying up all the materials therefor over those treacherous trails where a slip would have spelled death. Among the materials that were so carried up with infinite patience and labor were wooden beams, 40 feet long and 16 inches square, brought from the San Mateo mountains 20 miles away. The earth for the cemetery was brought up sackful by sackful, for the 80 acre top of the rock of Acoma is entirely bare of soil.

The trail used by Father Juan is still in use and is known as *el camino del padre*.

The Bell of the San Miguel

Entering Santa Fe from the east on the old Spanish trails highway, we pass on the right-hand side of the narrow, old-world street and just south of the musical rivulet known as the Santa Fe river a little church so nearly hidden by the intervening shrubbery that it is likely to escape notice.

It is the ancient chapel of San Miguel – the oldest existing church in the United States, and certainly the most interesting. The exact year of its erection is not known but it was not later than 1608. It was built for a colony of Tlascalan Indians who had migrated from Mexico along with Oñate's Spanish colony in 1598 and had settled on the south side of the Santa Fe river.

The interior of this old church was burned by the Pueblo Indians in the rebellion of 1680, but the walls which were of adobe brick were not damaged. The interior woodwork was replaced and the church restored to service – this time for the white population of Santa Fe – between 1693 and 1710.

The object of greatest interest in that old church is a fine bell known as the bell of the San Miguel. It is intact and in perfectly serviceable condition, but it is not now in service on the ground that it is too valuable to be exposed to possible damage. It reposes in the rear of the church under the choir loft. Its weight is 780 pounds, but the bell is not as large as one would assume from its weight since its walls are four inches thick.

Its story, partly legendary, partly historical, follows.

In the year 711 the Moors from Africa invaded Spain and thereafter, for nearly eight centuries, Spain waged an intermittent warfare with these moslem invaders. Little by little the Moors pushed their dominion farther and farther over Spanish territory, until they had nearly the entire realm under their sway. As often as Spain rebelled against their overlordship she was defeated and the alien rule became more and more tyrannical.

In 1356 the Spanish were engaged in one of these revolutions — one that at the start bore some promise of success. But now the cross was being defeated in battle after battle with the crescent, and the situation was becoming desperate. The people knew that if they should fail in this struggle, the exactions and oppressions of their conquerors would become more crushing than ever.

So the people of one city that lay in the pathway of the victorious infidels assembled in one great conclave and there vowed a costly bell to Saint Joseph if he would lend his aid in checking and overcoming the moslems.

The mold was prepared for casting the bell and when the metal therefor was molten, the people cast their gold and silver ornaments of every sort into it. This precious increment so swelled the volume of the metal that the bell had to be cast four inches thick in order to use all of it.

The bell, when finished and taken from the mold, was found to have a tone of surpassing sweetness — "the richness of gold and the sweetness of sacrifice."

It was mounted in the tower of a church dedicated to Saint Joseph and with its first ringing the power of the Moors began to decline. The crescent began to sink before the cross. Thereafter for 136 years the bell sounded its beautiful peals – miraculously, it is said – whenever the Christians gained a victory over the Moors. It so sounded for the last time when in 1492 the last moorish stronghold fell before the combined armies of Castile and Aragon.

Then, probably about the year 1530, the bell was brought to Mexico where for an additional century it rang the birth of christianity in the New World. From Mexico it was brought up the Grande river by Nicolas Ortiz Nino Ladron de Guevara – one of the wealthy Spanish hidalgos who emigrated to the newly-occupied province of New Mexico – and later installed in the Ortiz chapel in Santa Fe.

The Ortiz chapel was destroyed during the rebellion of 1680 and when the province was reoccupied in 1693 this bell was taken to the San Miguel chapel and hung in the tower. There it remained for nearly two centuries. In 1872 the tower of the San Miguel was damaged by a storm and the bell was removed to the interior of the church where it since has reposed.

This bell bears the inscription in relief, "San José ruega por nos" (Saint Joseph, pray for us) followed by the date, "Ogusto 9 de 1356" (august 9, 1356).

The Reverend W. J. Howlett declares that this is "the sweetest-toned bell in America, and perhaps the richest." The present writers can testify as to the wonderful purity of its tone. When struck sharply with a hammer, its note is mellow and pleasing, carrying with it a suggestion of "the hush of cloisters and the sigh of renunciation," yet a light tap of a child's finger nail will wake a response.

Doubts have been expressed regarding the age of this bell. But the date thereon should, it seems, settle the question for the inscription is in relief. If the date is a forgery, then the forgery is as old as the bell for that date was placed upon the bell by the mould in which it was cast. It is possible that the bell at some time may have been broken and been recast with its original inscription, but even this we very much doubt.

To appreciate its age one has only to remember that it was cast in the year the battle of Poitiers was fought, and Agincourt was 60 years in the future. It antedated Joan of Arc by nearly a century and was more than a century old when the eastern Roman empire fell before the Turk. The great Florentine artists, da Vinci, Michelangelo, and Raphael were not yet born at the time this bell first sounded and the discovery of America was one and one-third centuries in the future.

Sangre de Cristo

Northeastward from Santa Fe rises the most majestic mountains in New Mexico – the Sangre de Cristo (Blood of Christ) range – their peaks towering 12,000 to 14,000 feet above sea-level and 5,000 to 7,000 feet above the Rio Grande valley. The splendor of the sunset colors flung back by those towering masses of rock is said to be unsurpassed anywhere in the world. To the writers, those vivid dyes have at times suggested a great conflagration.

The following legend relates how the mountains received their name. Twenty-one missionaries were killed on that memorable august day and the visitor to Santa Fe may see there the enormous Cross of the Martyrs, erected as a memorial to these murdered priests. – C.H.

Picked out by dim torchlight in the kiva [31] of the Kah-po pueblo there shone brown Tehua faces, moist with perspiration and tense with excitement. Facing this council of the pueblo stood O-yeg-a-pi, the war shaman of the village, haranguing his auditors. From his uplifted right hand dangled two ropes, one of palmilla fiber tied with many knots, no two alike, and the other a leathern thong carrying fourteen knots, all alike. [32]

[31] The kiva, also called estufa, was the council room of the Pueblo Indians. It usually was subterranean and circular in ground plan with the entrance in the roof.

[32] These ropes have puzzled students. According to statements made later

Within these secret walls only the quick breathing of his listeners could be heard as O-yeg-a-pi paused in his deep-throated argument to study the expressions of the eyes fixed upon him.

A young warrior with a scar across his cheek moved restlessly as if desiring to interrupt the speaker. But it was not proper that he should speak, except to ask questions, until the older men voiced their opinions.

O-yeg-a-pi continued:

"Our gods have promised the great Po-pé in the kiva of Taos that they will help us to destroy these strangers who strive to force their gods upon us, and will restore to us the freedom of our forefathers who have gone to *shipapu!*"

"You see in this one rope, my brothers, that in fourteen more days we are to rise and rid ourselves of our oppressors! In this other, twenty and four of the thirty and eight knots have been loosed! Twenty and four pueblos already have signified that they will rise on that day! And here, my brothers, is our knot – the thrice-looped knot of Kah-po! Bid me untie it, and so join ourselves with the other pueblos in destroying our white overlords!"

The young brave now spoke:

"What of the pueblos of Shie-whib-ak and Ka-tish-tya? [33] What of the pueblos of the Piros and Tompiros?"

The question enraged O-yeg-a-pi.

by the Indians, Po-pé's messenger carried a rope (of palmilla fiber according to some witnesses, a leathern thong according to others) on which was tied a number of knots signifying the number of days to elapse before the uprising, and each pueblo joining the conspiracy untied one of the knots. But had this been done, the rope would have had no significance unless but one pueblo were admitted per day.

The explanation we offer was given us by an Indian of Tesuque in 1927, and since it removes the apparent confusion, we have tentatively accepted it.

[33] The pueblos of Isleta and San Felipe.

"They are dogs and the sons of dogs!" he snarled. "They are the friends of the white people! The Piros and Tompiros are not to have the honor of joining us, and the invitation of Po-pé has not been extended to them. When we have won our freedom, the hand of our wrath shall be laid upon the people of Ka-tish-tya and Shie-whib-ak and their bones shall whiten upon their mesas!"

"Now, my brothers," O-yeg-a-pi continued, "speak! Po-pé's messenger waits, and this rope must carry our voice to the remaining pueblos and back to our leader!"

The presumptious young brave spoke again:

"Padre Juan has taught us much that is good for us to know and has taught us no evil. Neither have his gods harmed us!"

The shaman replied sharply,

"Our leader, Po-pé, has said that all the white people must die or he will come on the wings of his victory and destroy us!"

When every one save him of the scarred cheek had voiced his consent, all stood silent while O-yeg-a-pi, holding the ropes aloft, slowly untied the knot that represented Kah-po and handed the cords to the messenger who had stood immovable awaiting the action of the conclave. Silently the lean youth disappeared up the ladder to the entrance of the kiva to continue his journey to the remaining pueblos.

For three hours thereafter the men of Kah-po remained in conference, carefully planning the blow that was to accomplish the destruction of all the white people within their territories.

Just before the assembly disbanded a sudden command from O-yeg-a-pi brought three warriors to their feet around the young man with the scarred cheek. Then swiftly and surely the deed was done and the defender of Padre Juan lay sprawled on the floor of the kiva, writhing in death agony.

"Even so," muttered O-yeg-a-pi, "did our leader Po-pé to his own son who refused to give his voice in favor of freedom!" [34]

"Our faith is as old as the great peaks that mount the eastern sky," said the war shaman to that mysterious council of old men gathered in the kiva of Kah-po on august 9, 1680. "Yet our children wish to turn their faces to the unknown gods of the white priest. Only this day I heard him planting disbelief in the hearts of our little ones. But for the diligence of us who know the truth, his followers would be many instead of few."

It now wanted but three days until the day set for the uprising and O-yeg-a-pi held in his hand a rope on which but three knots remained. Each evening, for eleven days, one knot had been loosed by O-yeg-a-pi in the presence of this council of old men. He now continued, bitterly,

"In a dream it was revealed to me that some of our bravest young men – even a few of those who this hour watch from the high places for sight of our chief's messengers – secretly wish to spare the life of the alien priest. He has won their favor by taking part in their games and by teaching them the evil arts that he learned in his home across the great water.

"For near to 100 years our people have longed for their old liberty! Now all is ready! None shall be spared! The priest of the new gods must die too!"

[34] Po-pé had killed his own son-in-law, the governor of the San Juan pueblo, for suspected sympathy toward the Spaniards.

At that moment an Indian appeared in the opening above their heads and rapidly descended the ladder. The entire assembly rose in alarm as this intruder sprang to the floor.

"Our plans have been betrayed!" he exclaimed breathlessly. "Two young men from Kah-po have fled and carried the warning to the ruler of the white people! Runners from among our people there have carried this news to Po-pé and his fire signals have just reached our watchers, telling us to rise and strike! No time is to be lost! Even now the fire signals are leaping from mountain top to mountain top, to Acoma, to Zuñi, to the Moqui, bidding the pueblos rise and strike at once!"

All now was confusion in the kiva. Above the babbling of the old men, fiercely rose the exultant voice of O-yeg-a-pi:

"We are free, my brothers! We are free! Let us be at our work! Let us strike down the priest of the unknown god!"

Soon the pueblo of Kah-po was shaken from its afternoon drowsiness and transformed into a deathtrap for the few Spaniards who were there. The Tehua women, unaware of the plot until the very instant of the onslaught, either gathered their children into the protection of their homes or snatched up clubs and stones and joined the vengeful men. O-yeg-a-pi, with knife drawn, and followed by a mob of bloodthirsty warriors, ran toward the mission church on the outskirts of the village. Some of the Indians stopped at the locked door of the main entrance to prevent Padre Juan's escape, while the rest led by O-yeg-a-pi passed around to the sacristy entry. A few feet from the door the natives stopped and waited. Throughout the village came the sounds of struggle; the exultant yells of the maddened savages and the terrified cries of their victims, for all Indians known to be in sympathy with the whites were slain along with the Spaniards.

On the morning of that fateful day Padre Juan had gone about his duties as usual. He had been assigned, at his own request, to the Kah-po pueblo – a village of the Tehua tribe having about 800 native inhabitants and reputed to be one of the most unruly and obstinate villages in the whole of New Mexico.

Now he had been for several years striving faithfully with the people of Kah-po, and thus far he had few real conversions as the fruits of his labors. Most of the village was nominally within the church, but in secret the people still practiced their pagan rites and served their pagan gods.

Padre Juan lately had heard vague rumors of some kind of conspiracy among the Indians but when he questioned his neophytes, they professed entire ignorance of any movement inimical to the Spaniards and assured him of their unshakable devotion.

On this day he was filled with renewed courage for never before had his brown people been so kindly, so solicitous, so attentive to his admonitions as they had during and after mass that morning. Padre Juan accepted this as a good omen, not suspecting that it was but the purring of the panther that, with muscles tensing, was gathering itself for a spring.

Late in the afternoon he had gone to the church to prepare for the evening service. For some time he had lingered about the altar, when he became cognizant of a rising tumult of yelling and commotion in the village. He left the altar and approached the sacristy door to see what the uproar was about. As he opened the door he was confronted by a swarm of the hostile natives.

"What does this mean, my children?" he asked in astonishment.

For answer O-yeg-a-pi sprang forward with knife uplifted.

"Let your god help you now!" he yelled, driving the knife into Padre Juan's breast.

The priest sank down in the doorway. A wild howl rose from the throats of the Indians.

"This is being dealt to all of your accursed race this day!" screamed O-yeg-a-pi, leaping over the body of the stricken priest into the church. He was followed by a score of the warriors. There they hurled to the floor the sacred statues and images, and then rushed out to execute a dance of thanksgiving to their gods.

Padre Juan, with his lifeblood creeping over the ground, thought not of himself. The agonizing realization that rose in his mind was that all his high hopes, his prayers, and his labors had gone for naught. Among those frenzied Indians dancing in joy in front of his church were some who had been his most faithful neophytes, some whom he had believed his steadfast friends. Now they were rejoicing in his death. The sublime dream of the great order of Saint Francis was fading in blood. The cross was down, satan triumphant!

Such were the thoughts that swept through the mind of the dying priest. And then there came to him a sudden hope that he might know, before oblivion shrouded him, whether this were a temporary or a final defeat; whether the cross should arise again, militant and victorious; or whether this land were to remain forever in darkness. He raised his weakened arms and with all his soul prayed for a sign.

Even as his tortured lips gasped this prayer, a

crimson splendor leaped from the peaks of the great
mountain range that towered in the east and the eastern
sky was dyed with living, pulsating hues! Now, as the
whole heavens and earth became suffused with the mysterious red radiance, the Indians were stricken mute
and O-yeg-a-pi, casting off the religious vestments that
he had seized in the church, fled terror-stricken to the
darkness of the kiva.

And when the indian women went about robbing the
bodies of the slain they saw upon the face of Padre
Juan such a look of holy calm that they forebore to
touch his garments. Even the indian men to whom was
assigned the task of burying the victims of the massacre
forbore to touch the body of Padre Juan and instead
of carrying him out for burial, they heaped earth upon
the body where it lay.

Fidelity to this legend requires that we set it in the
pueblo of Kah-po – now the indian village of Santa
Clara. But at the time of the massacre there was no
resident priest at Kah-po and there is no record of any
priest having been killed there.

However, at the pueblos of Tesuque and Taos priests
named Juan were killed and from either of these two
pueblos the Sangre de Cristo mountains appear much
more majestic than from Santa Clara. Moreover, it
was from Indians of Tesuque that the Spanish in Santa
Fe received warning.[35] It is our opinion, therefore, that
this legend somehow strayed from home and that its
incidents, if true, occurred at Tesuque.

[35] These two Tesuque Indians did not voluntarily reveal the plot to the
Spaniards. Having been sent by Po-pé to communicate details of the conspiracy to the Tanos pueblos, the Tanos chiefs betrayed the messengers to
Governor Otermin who had the two arrested and questioned. To save their
own lives they revealed the entire plot.

La Conquistadora

During the twelve years following the Pueblo rebellion of 1680, several attempts were made by the Spanish to reoccupy New Mexico but not one advance penetrated as far as Santa Fe before being compelled to retreat.

Then Diego de Vargas was commissioned to undertake the task. When in 1692 he made a preliminary expedition up the Rio Grande, by the exercise of tact and goodwill he secured the submission of all the pueblos without having to strike a blow.

But when he returned the following year with a larger force and a company of colonists, several of the pueblos, misled by a few malcontents into believing that the Spaniards intended taking a bloody revenge for the disaster of 1680, became hostile and it was necessary for De Vargas to subdue them by force of arms. His little army of Spanish soldiers would have been entirely inadequate for this task had it not been for the aid of indian allies from various pueblos.

The most desperate battle fought by De Vargas in subduing the belligerents occurred at Santa Fe. Upon arriving there he had found the Indians in possession of the city around a portion of which, including the plaza and the *palacio,* they had built a substantial wall.[36]

It was winter and De Vargas's men were suffering

---

[36] Santa Fe was being held by the Tanos Indians, but they were reinforced by warriors from the Tehua and Cuares pueblos.

greatly from lack of shelter. He very civilly asked the Indians of Santa Fe to return to their pueblos so that his soldiers could find quarters in the buildings of Santa Fe. But they, mistaking his forbearance for cowardice, answered him with defiance.

De Vargas thereupon began arranging his forces for an attack. Both sides felt that this would be the decisive conflict of the whole campaign. Hostile pueblos had been heavily drawn upon for warriors, while De Vargas had, in addition to his own soldiers, allies from six friendly pueblos. Shortly before beginning the attack, his forces were augmented by the arrival of the entire warrior body of the then powerful pueblo of Cicuyé under their veteran chief, Juan Ye.

Throughout the day the battle raged; the Indians of Santa Fe delivering their heaviest blows against the Cicuyéan warriors, who under their old chief held their ground like seasoned European infantry. One attack by the indian cavalry against the Cicuyéan position assumed serious proportions, but it soon was broken and scattered by the Spanish cavalry.

Night fell upon a drawn battle. The Indians of Santa Fe had suffered heavily, but they remained in possession of the city and had fought off all assaults.

De Vargas, in his march up the Rio Grande valley, had carried with him in a closed wagon a beautiful statue of the Virgin Mary; and wherever his army went into camp he caused to be erected a little sanctuary to shelter the holy image.[37] He believed that the Mother of Christ aided him in his campaigns and inclined the victory to him.

---

[37] The remains of several of these little wayside sanctuaries are still to be seen. The best preserved one is a few miles southwest of Santa Fe.

So now in the evening after that first day's battle De Vargas, in the presence of his entire army standing with presented arms, knelt before this statue and made a solemn promise that if the Holy Mother would aid him in the battle of the morrow and give him a victory, he would cause to be erected on that spot a beautiful sanctuary for her statue, and that once each year in commemoration the statue should be carried in state from its resting place in the principal church of Santa Fe to this sanctuary and there be left for nine days to receive the praises and adoration of the people.

The next morning De Vargas advanced with his whole force and after a feint at a general attack suddenly concentrated his forces and struck the west wall of the fortification. After a desperate conflict lasting but a few minutes, the wall was carried, De Vargas himself being the first man over.

The rebels, seeing their fortifications successfully stormed, became panic-stricken and soon all resistance was ended. The native governor of the town, realizing that all was lost, hanged himself, while his warriors were scattered far and wide. None was slain after resistance ended, although De Vargas had difficulty in restraining his infuriated allies from wreaking a summary vengeance upon the vanquished.

De Vargas later executed the ring-leaders of the revolt, but he would permit no punishment to be visited upon the conquered pueblos.

He then remembered his vow – De Vargas was a man who always kept his promises – and the sanctuary was built on the very spot where his army had been encamped before Santa Fe.

This sanctuary, the chapel of Nuestra Señora del

Rosario (Our Lady of the Rosary) still stands in the city of Santa Fe but has been considerably altered in recent years. De Vargas's statue of the Virgin Mary first was placed in the San Miguel church, and later in the church of San Francisco and once each year, after the reconquest, it was carried at the head of a ceremonial procession to the Rosario chapel and there left for nine days, according to De Vargas's vow, and the nine-day period was given over to merry-making, religious ceremonials, and a general fiesta.

This annual ceremony of escorting the statue (the same statue that De Vargas carried but now called *La Conquistadora*) from the church (now cathedral) of San Francisco to the Rosario chapel still is carried out and it is said there has been no break in the observance since 1693. It is the most interesting feature of the annual Santa Fe fiesta of today, which itself is really the survival of the fiesta inaugurated by De Vargas. Fifteen hundred to two thousand people take part in the procession escorting *La Conquistadora*. The statue now is left in the Rosario chapel one week instead of nine days.

Doctor L. B. Prince states that one day of the fiesta, known as De Vargas Day, is the first annual legal holiday ever established within the limits of the United States. He cites archive no. 179 of the Congressional library as containing the proclamation by Governor Penuela in 1712 of this holiday, the proclamation directing that the holiday be observed that year and each year thereafter.

El Jardin de las Cruces

The tragedy that gave a name to what is now a modern little city of New Mexico, while generally known in the valley of the Rio Grande, is little known elsewhere and never has appeared in print except in the form of a very brief synopsis.

Details of the tragedy are preserved in the lore of some of the Spanish-americans of Mesilla and Las Cruces. The account of the ambush and massacre is the authors', but it is in accord with the tactics of the Apache, and the actual attack must have been as described in all important features. – C.H.

A party of colonists bound for northern New Mexico was nearing its promised land. For three weary months it had been crawling its way over the plateaus and mountain valleys of Zacatecas, Durango, and Chihuahua. There remained now hardly more than the Jornada desert to be traversed; in ten more days these people would again be with their kind in the fertile new lands of their dreams.

Their spirits rose with every league left behind them; laughter and dancing were beginning to take the place of vigilance and discipline. They had encountered only friendly Indians as far as El Paso del Norte; beyond that point they thus far had encountered none. They had come to regard the grave and emphatic warnings given them by the officials at Chihuahua and Carrizal as merely jokes of the brand usually told to newcomers to affright them. They even regarded it as a joke with some hidden catch to it, when the captain of the garrison at El Paso offered them a military escort.

Probably the awakening of spring also contributed to the relaxation of vigilance. Wild flowers were springing into bloom along the trail; the cat's-claw was a mass of pink or yellow, burdening the air with its exotic perfume; song birds warbled and made love among the shrubbery. All nature bespoke renewed life; nothing suggested death.

Yet from the time this caravan entered the sandhills north of El Paso until it reached its final camping-ground it was under constant surveillance by reptilian-eyed Apache scouts who moved as silently and invisibly as gliding snakes. The main body of Indians, some 50 in number, moved parallel to the road but kept several miles therefrom in order to avoid the possibility of detection. Their scouts, taking up advantageous positions on the trail ahead of the caravan, scrutinized it intently as it passed; then, making a wide detour, again found a hiding-place ahead. The travelers thus were watched constantly every hour of the day and every detail of their number, livestock, equipment, and armament was studied by these unseen spies and reported to the chiefs.

The keen perception of the savage was quick to note the let-down of vigilance in the caravan. On the evening of the third day out from El Paso, the Apaches in council agreed that the time had come to strike; their spies had reported the travelers encamped on a spot surrounded by sand mounds, mesquite thickets, and tall clumps of salt-grass – ideal setting for an ambush – and that they had thrown out no pickets.

Hiding their horses in a canyon a mile above the encampment, the Apaches under cover of a moonless night and moving silently as shadows gradually encompassed the sleeping camp, drawing their coil stealthily closer and closer until they were almost within stone's throw of the caravan. Then each Indian made himself as nearly invisible as possible and silently waited for the day.[38]

With the first gleam of dawn in the east the camp was astir. The people were eager to get on. The smouldering camp fires were refueled, pots and pans appeared, the women busied themselves preparing a breakfast of *atole,* fresh *conejo,* and chocolate. The men hurried about packing camp equipment into the wagons; the children romped and tumbled about the fires and clamored for food.

Yet there were unmistakable portents of the peril overhanging these people, had there been one person among them capable of interpreting those signs. There were no tracks of Indians; the Apaches were far too cunning to leave any visible spoor near the trail. The most sensitive human ear, the most penetrating human eye could have detected nothing actually indicative of the presence of the enemy. Yet, had there been one experienced rider of the trail in the party, at the first break of dawn he would have hurried the people into the shelter of their wagons and would have thrown out

[38] The reader may wonder why the Indians did not now fall upon the sleeping camp. We do not know. But until they finally learned the advantage of night attacks from the Spaniards, they would not open their ambushes until daylight. It has been asserted that the Apaches and Comanches had a superstitious fear of night fighting.

a strong party of mounted men to uncover the ambush, knowing that Apaches on foot invariably would flee from mounted, armed men.

For the keen eyes of the little native folk – the small animals and birds of the desert – had with the first blush of day, or even before, detected the hidden savages. These denizens of the wilderness paid little heed to the animal that walked abroad openly in the light of day, but they instinctively feared the animal that lurked. To them these concealed Indians were animals stalking their prey, hence, animals to be feared, watched, and avoided.

Consequently, there were no rabbits hopping leisurely through the bushes in search of breakfast; they all were in hiding. The prairie dogs were not saluting the dawn with their usual chirruping; they were silent in their burrows. The morning song-birds were mute, or else gave voice only to an occasional note of alarm or warning.

These were the signs that would have galvanized an experienced traveler into instant action. But these people, untutored in the language of the desert, joyously sat themselves down to their breakfast under the very shadow of death, oblivious to the warning cry of nature, "You are in deadly peril!"

Then the shadow descended and enfolded them. The silence was rent by the cracking of musketry, the whine and thud of balls, the whirr of agate-tipped arrows, the guttural cry of stricken men. The unhurt men sprang up, bewildered; then instinctively rushed to the wagons for their muskets; the women, terrified beyond articulate speech, huddled together into one hysterical mass; the children frantically sought their mothers in a panic of uncomprehending fear. The shaken men, without leadership, without any prearranged plan of action, fired futilely at the puffs of smoke instead of mounting and endeavouring to ride the savages down. To this, add the demoralizing effect of complete surprise, and there could have been but the one event.

With resistance ended, the savages rose from their ambush and charged the camp. They wasted no precious ammunition. Wounded men, women, and children were clubbed to death, the exultant screeches of the Indians drowning the screams of their victims.

The goods in the wagons then were ransacked, the wagons fired, and, driving the horses and cattle before them, the savages made for the canyon where their mounts were concealed. Within two hours they had forded the Rio Grande and were heading for the Mimbres mountains wherein pursuit would be impossible.

A lone Piros Indian, riding up the trail, heard the firing and hurried forward to ascertain the cause. Then, unable to render any assistance himself, he turned back on the trail and struck a steady swinging gallop that carried him to El Paso before noon, where he reported the caravan surrounded and in a desperate plight, but holding its own. A mounted squad of soldiers at once was hurried northward to assist the caravan but when, with their horses roweled and exhausted, they reached the scene they found only death and desolation.

The faces of these men paled under their tan at sight of the women and children. The corpses of mothers still held, tightly clasped in their arms, the mutilated bodies of their children, having endeavored to the last to give them the protection that their children had confidently expected of them.

These soldiers were silent. Nothing they could have said would have helped. The victims were beyond the need of prayers or tears; their assassins beyond the reach of avenging steel.

Silently the men began preparing the graves.

But the following year those same soldiers were in the command of Governor-general Mogollon in his relentless campaign against the savages and they remembered what they had seen at Las Cruces. By the time the campaign was over the savages, too, had cause to remember. It is said that in that campaign the Spanish soldiers showed no quarter, and killed women as well as men.

Several versions of the legend differ slightly in their details. One version states that the caravan was one of traders and their families; another has it that an Indian of El Paso had detected the savages stalking the caravan and had reported it to the officers at El Paso, whereupon a mounted squad was dispatched to overtake and escort the caravan through the Jornada desert. Still another version states that it was another company of travelers, and not of soldiers, that first came upon the scene.

The victims of that massacre, it is said, were buried just east of the trail and a small cross of mesquite wood was erected at the head of each grave, the name of the victim, where ascertainable, being cut on the cross. It was some years later that the spot became known as the garden of the crosses. One party of travelers, while encamped near by, cleared the weeds from the graves. Another party laid a border of stones around the garden and the little cemetery was kept neat and orderly by various parties who camped there from time to time.[39]

For about a century that little garden of crosses stood there 50 miles from any human habitation. No relatives or friends of those who slept beneath the crosses ever visited them, for they were a thousand miles from any of their kindred. Strangers tended the graves and replaced broken crosses, and strangers gave the little *campo santo* (holy encampment) its beautful name that forms the title of this story.

There is a tradition that the church plaza in the heart of the present city of Las Cruces contains the original garden of crosses, and that the whole of this plaza was a cemetery a century ago. This tradition may be true for the old Spanish road ran right along the west side of that plaza.

When a village grew up there, for a time it was known as *La Aldea del Jardin de las Cruces* (the little town of the garden of crosses). Later this became shortened to Las Cruces.

If the massacre occurred while Mogollon was governor of New Mexico, it took place between the years 1712 and 1715, most probably in 1712, for it was in 1713 that Mogollon conducted his campaign against the savages.

We find no historical evidence that this massacre occurred. But that means nothing. Most of the archives of New Mexico were destroyed or otherwise disposed

---

[39] This is quite in keeping with the character of both Mexicans and Spaniards. They reverenced the dead. Travelers along this road always placed additional stones upon any new grave they encountered, and thus in a short time every grave was marked by a symmetrical mound of stones.

of in the years 1869-1871 and as a result there are many blank pages in New Mexico's history. There was a massacre at Tomé in 1779, concerning which we would know nothing were it not for a record of the burial of the victims, found in the archives of the San Felipe church in Albuquerque. A massacre at Fernandez de Taos would be known only to legend were it not that Governor Anza mentioned it in a letter. Miera, who made a map of New Mexico in 1779, wrote across the beautiful valle de rio San Antonio, "Settlements destroyed by Comanches." Were it not for that, we should not know that there ever were any Spanish towns along the rio San Antonio in New Mexico. Morfi, in his description of New Mexico (1780) names a number of settlements that had been ravaged by the Apaches and Comanches, but his narrative contains the only mention of those settlements that exists.

Aguilar and Ysabel

More feared than all other tribes by the Spanish in New Mexico were the Apaches. The Utes and Navajos were too far away to be a very serious menace and the Comanches would keep a treaty as long as they remembered it, which is more than the white race has done. But the Apaches were a perennial terror. Campaigns against them brought only temporary relief for they observed a treaty only so long as was advantageous to them, and they were as cordially hated by other tribes as by the Spaniards.

The following is but one of the many similar stories of tragedy written by the Apaches on the Spanish and later Mexican frontier of New Mexico. – C. H.

About the year 1775 the district around Sevillita, New Mexico, was one of the most attractive in the province. The overland caravans from Chihuahua furnished the settlers with such necessities as they could not themselves produce. While across the mountains ranged the Apaches and Navajos, there stood on the brow of a hill the little barracks with its garrison of seasoned fighters, guaranteeing peace to the settlement clustered under its protection. The watchtower with openings on the west, north, and east sides, commanded a view of the country for several miles in those directions – a fact that the savages more than once had discovered to their discomfiture.

Now came Aguilar Mentona up from Mexico, with his bride Ysabel, seeking a livelihood in the new land.

There was a very fertile belt of land half a league down the valley from the settlement, southward from the watchtower. A portion of this land Aguilar secured and on it proceeded to build a home for his bride and himself. He had taken counsel with her and she was not afraid, notwithstanding the warnings of their friends that they were getting too far away from protection.

Aguilar built his walls of stone, leaving a loophole on each side through which guns could be fired. His windows he placed high on the walls and barred them securely with bands of wrought iron hammered out for him by the christian Indians of Isleta. He left but one doorway in his outer walls and in this he placed a heavy door of thick mesquite that would defy assault indefinitely.

Into this new home Aguilar took Ysabel and the two were content. In the daytime he worked his fields without fear and rejoiced in the luxuriant vegetation that because of his labor and care was blossoming into life on his acres. On sundays he and Ysabel attended mass at the church in town and visited with their village friends afterward.

The two often had discussed the possibility of an indian attack. Aguilar possessed two muskets and two pistols. Ysabel was as skilled in the handling of these arms as was he. It was agreed that in the event of an attack, Ysabel should defend the loophole in the east wall and Aguilar that in the west and, finally, if escape or rescue was hopeless, Aguilar was to kill his wife and then himself. Better a thousand times to die in that manner than to fall into the hands of the fiends whose methods of torture were more horrible than anything the white man ever was capable of devising.

With this possibility in mind Aguilar frequently withdrew the powder and bullets from the two pistols and reloaded them with fresh charges, looking always carefully to the priming so that by no chance would they misfire.

Aguilar had finished harvesting his fields which had yielded liberally to his care. The little stone shed that he had built to shelter his crops proved too small and the yield overflowed into one room of his house. So the two faced the winter contentedly with no misgivings.

Then one blustery, windy night – a north wind that would prevent musketry fire from being heard in the village – the inevitable happened. Aguilar and Ysabel were awakened by the hellish screeches of a band of Apaches – apparently a large band – and a flight of arrows crashed through one of their windows to an accompaniment of falling glass.

A moment later the two were at their posts, each with a musket. Ysabel needed no words of encouragement from Aguilar, and he checked them before they were uttered. Her nerve was as steady and her head as cool, as his.

The Apaches, as was their custom, were racing around and around the house, discharging their arrows into the windows and occasionally at the two loopholes through which the defenders were firing. Whenever the shadowy form of an Indian appeared in the darkness, he was greeted with a shot, but aim was difficult and only a few of the shots found their mark. That one now and then did was attested by the occasional howl of agony from some disabled warrior.

An hour passed, and the two had succeeded in keeping the fiends at bay. The Indians finally ceased their screeching, and no more arrows came through the windows. The man and wife first grew hopeful, then exultant. They believed they had beaten the savages off.

After a while Aguilar moved to unbar the door to take a view of the outside, but Ysabel cautioned him to wait. Possibly the Apaches were awaiting just such a move. So the two remained quiet and listened.

Then, all at once, above the whistling of the wind, they heard the crackling of flames! Their one vulnerable point had been attacked; their roof had been fired!

The illumination furnished by the blazing roof soon picked out the Indians distinctly, and the two defenders fought with the frenzy of desperation. Aguilar lighted a candle that they might be able to load their muskets more rapidly. More of the Indians fell and the remainder after a few minutes withdrew to the front of the house, where they could not be fired upon, to await the moment when the flames should drive their victims into their hands.

Aguilar now seized an axe and began to hew frantically at the door in an effort to cut a loophole through. But the tough, seasoned wood that he had selected to defy the savages now defied him. Before he could cut a hole through the obstinate mesquite, a side of his roof collapsed into the adjoining room, carrying down a portion of the ceiling with it. This was followed by the sound of a hellish screeching from the waiting Indians. They had not long now to wait for the heat inside the room was becoming nearly intolerable.

Ysabel turned to her husband with a mute question in her eyes, and he shook his head. They could hope for no assistance for the one side of the barracks lookout containing no window faced in their direction!

Ysabel laid down her musket and, with white face but resolute eyes, came to Aguilar. He dropped his axe and seized one of the pistols.

"*Adios, amorita! adios!*" He kissed her passionately.

"Quickly, Aguilar! We shall go to heaven together – always together!"

Aguilar's pistol rang out and the form he was holding in his arms shuddered convulsively, then became limp.

At that moment a volley of musketry came above the roar of the flames, followed by the howls of the fleeing savages. Laying the body of his wife gently down, Aguilar sprang to the door and unbarred it. Outside were mounted men – his friends, who had seen his blazing roof from afar and had ridden hard to his rescue. They greeted him with shouts and with a waving of muskets.

Aguilar did not answer. He staggered back into the furnace that had been his home, and closed the door. A moment later a second pistol shot rang out, and hard upon it came the crash of the roof.

It was at about this time that the Apaches first adopted night attacks. In earlier days, as we have noted, they attacked only in the daytime. They were continually picking off isolated homes and tiny settlements; yet when Governor Anza in 1779 attempted to concentrate the people into compact villages, at the expense of the crown, they protested bitterly and even carried their protests to the viceroy who let them have their way.– C.H.

Texas Legends

Texas Legends

The state of Texas has an abundance of legendary lore, much of which, however, dates from the Anglo-american colonial period.

Treasure legends outnumber all others together. Like the treasure legends of New Mexico, these appear to be pure fiction and are much alike with similar basic plots. Most of them are based upon, or derive their inspiration from, the tradition of buried silver bullion taken from a rich mine in the San Saba region during the middle eighteenth century, a mine that had no existence in fact.

Among the Mexicans of the San Antonio valley are found many charming little legends of the "Blue Lady" never yet collected but which ought to be preserved in the literature of the southwest.

The state has a number of other legends dating from the Spanish period, several of which are well known within the state but practically unknown elsewhere. Of those reproduced, each has appeared one or more times in print, but only in outline form or hardly that. A writer pays his reader a compliment in assuming that he already knows these legends, but perhaps some of our readers, like ourselves, would be willing to exchange the compliment for the complete story.

In addition to those which have been selected for this volume, there are other meritorious ones which at least deserve mention: "The wraith of San Luis pass," "The padre's beacon," "The voices of the San José," "Ghosts of the Alamo," "The mine of the redlands," and "The mortar of the Mission Concepción."

The Margil Vine

The venerable Fray Antonio Margil, the first *padre presidente* of the Texas missions, established the San Antonio de Valero in 1716 and was its *padre superior* while in Texas. Margil was a man of exceptional ability and culture, and his powers as an orator were known throughout the catholic world. He won his reputation as a missionary-teacher in Central America, and in 1687 was made president of the college of Queretaro in Mexico. In 1706 he was selected to found the college of Zacatecas which he served as president until his assignment to Texas in 1716. From 1723 until his death in 1726 he was acting president of the college of Guadalupe. He is buried in the cathedral of Mexico City. – C.H.

The little indian boy, Shavano, perched in the arms of a poplar tree that overlooked the Valero mission, sat moodily regarding the pictures which formed before his eyes in the smoke curling up from a hundred clustered indian cabins. Whenever Shavano became oppressed by the boastings of his more fortunate playmates, he sought refuge in the branches of this friendly old tree where he dreamed treasures of his own.

The parents of Shavano were very poor, but there was one tradition in the family that made them rich in pride and that helped to console the boy's heart at times like this when his poverty sat heavily upon him. They had lived, before coming to the Valero, at a mission on the Rio Grande and Shavano in his infancy had been given the part of the Christ-child in the christmas presentation of the nativity. He had delighted the padres with his quiet and gentle manner. Prior to that the mission padres had been compelled to use a wooden, painted image to represent the infant Jesus in his manger, for they could find no indian babies tractable enough to play the passive part of the Christ-child.

Now within three days, Shavano was to attend his sixth christmas program at the mission Valero and he had no gift worthy to offer to the holy infant. That was the problem weighing upon the boy's mind as he perched in the great poplar tree and watched the writhing streams of smoke. And as he restlessly snapped off twigs and dropped them through the branches of the tree, he felt resentful that through no fault of his own he should be deprived of the means of proving his loyalty.

But presently Shavano's reflections were interrupted by the sound of footsteps below, and he twisted about to see who was approaching. He looked down into the twinkling eyes of the saintly Padre Antonio Margil. The padre's face sobered as he observed the woebegone countenance of the boy. The two regarded each other for a moment in silence.

"Come down, my son," then invited the old priest, "and tell me what is troubling you."

Shavano obediently scrambled down from his perch. He stood staring at the brown earth at his feet, feeling ashamed that he had been found with tears in his eyes.

A few more encouraging words from Padre Antonio induced the boy to reveal the reason for his grief. As he enumerated his pitifully few possessions: a poorly-

balanced bow, a few crooked arrows, the tail feathers
of a blue jay, a handful of colored pebbles, from which
he must choose a gift for the Christ-child, he searched
the padre's face for signs of approval that might justify
the appearance of some one of the articles at the holy
manager. But Fray Margil's face did not change until
the boy had finished. Then he placed his hand on Shavano's head and assured him:

"It doesn't really matter about the gift, my son. A
gift is only a token that we give to show our love. If
you love the Christ-child in your heart, he knows it as
well as you do, and you need no gift to reveal your
loyalty to him."

The padre departed after a few more words of encouragement. But Shavano was not quite convinced.
He could not entirely understand the padre's reasoning.
Had not gifts always been the proofs of love and goodwill among his people? And had not all others taken
tokens of their love and loyalty to the chapel? He felt
that he must have something tangible to offer.

That night, wrapped in his ragged blanket beneath
the sky, he wished that he were able to reach up and
grasp one of those bright stars that were shining down
upon him, or one of the snowy, gossamer clouds that
drifted lazily overhead. Then he would have a gift fit
for the decoration of the manger of Bethlehem!

The next day Shavano still was unrelieved of his dis-
tress. The nearer approach of the festival – it was but
the next morning – served to increase his depression.

In this mood he wandered disconsolately to the edge
of the settlement, where stood his poplar tree, and
leaned against its trunk. After a while his attention was
drawn to a wisp of green at the foot of the tree and he

stooped to inspect it. It was a little vine, so tiny that it could have been trampled underfoot without being noticed.

Shavano pondered over the merits of the plant and concluded that it had none to speak of. Yet it would make a more suitable gift for the Christ-child than anything he possessed.

He walked to a low-hanging branch and broke off a substantial stick. With this he carefully dug up the plant. Then, hiding the little vine under his threadbare tunic, he hurried to his mother's collection of earthenware jars, selected one, and planted the vine in it, using soil like that from which the plant was taken.

Rather shamefacedly, he carried his gift to the mission chapel and surreptitiously placed it out of view among the more pretentious offerings about the manger.

It was the first time that the boy had seen the treasures on display there, and he lingered, fascinated by the marvelous assortment which represented incalculable wealth in his eyes. There were strings of beads and claws, blankets of gay colors, furs of small animals, brightly-dyed feathers, painted horns of buffalo, antelope, and deer, and many simple articles hand made by the Indians in the mission workshops. The one thing that Shavano regarded with greatest admiration, though, was a pair of great antlers that must have once belonged to some monarch of the forest. These were painted in more brilliant colors than the boy ever had seen before.

Then, suddenly becoming conscious of the pitiful insignificance of his own gift, Shavano turned and sneaked away, fearing that the Christ might be displeased at the poverty of the little weed-vine.

MISSION OF SAN ANTONIO DE VALERO

Reproduced from old plans, drawings, and descriptions

Before daybreak the next morning the christmas pageant of *Los pastores* [40] (the shepherds) was begun, starting with the appearance of the angels to the shepherds. This scene was enacted a league from the mission, in the presence of the whole indian population. As the shepherds wended their way to "Bethlehem," followed by their audience, Shavano experienced moments of delightful terror at the appearance of satan, who endeavored in various ways and at different times to divert the shepherds from their course. Shavano was amused by the sleepy, laggard shepherd who, whatever happened, always arrived on the scene just too late to witness it. But each time, Shavano's pleasure was abruptly terminated by recollection of the inadequacy of the gift he had left at the manger.

Over the chapel of the mission hung a great lamp, symbolizing the star of Bethlehem. Shavano was eager to witness the climaxing scene – the presentation of the Nativity of Christ – but, reluctant to appear as the donor of a worthless love-token, he hung back as the crowd approached the church doors.

He saw the doors swing back, as of their own accord, when the shepherds reached them, but he was surprised to see these actors stop and gaze fixedly within. Then to his ears there came the subdued cry, *milagro! milagro!* (miracle!)

Shavano wormed his way through the crowd. Perhaps, he thought, the Christ-child had bestowed some great blessing upon the donor of the wonderfully-painted antlers!

Before the doors of the chapel he halted, spellbound,

[40] This play still is enacted on christmas eve or morning in many Mexican communities of the southwest.

then his whole being quivered with ecstasy and tears of
joy sprang into his eyes. His little vine had grown miraculously; it had twined itself about and over the crib
of the infant Jesus, and had put forth a luxuriance of
bright green leaves and brilliant scarlet berries so that
it had become the most beautiful gift of all!

This vine, with its wintergreen leaves and red berries,
still grows in the San Antonio valley and, while the
botanists have a long and formidable name for it, to the
common people there it still is known as the Margil
vine. It is said and firmly believed by the Mexicans that
prior to the miraculous transformation of Shavano's
gift, the plant, wherever found, was an insignificant
one; but that afterward it became, as it is today, a vigorous, luxuriant perennial, suitable for shading porches
and arbors. Probably because of its legendary history,
the Margil vine is a favorite christmas decoration
among the Mexicans of that region.

The Sculptor of the San José

About the year 1696 there was born in Malaga, Spain, a boy named Juan Huisar who, tradition states, was a lineal descendant of the famous architect who designed the Alhambra.

His inherited talent for creative work manifested itself at an early age. He showed a decided preference for sculpture and his parents put him under the best instructors of the time. Juan first studied in Spain, then finished his work in Italy. Thus he grew up to young manhood and, when his studies in Italy were finished, he returned to Malaga.

There he became hopelessly ensnared by the bright eyes of the Señorita Iñes Yanez de Loja.

Iñes and Juan seemed to be devoted to each other, but Juan was poor and Iñes's parents objected to their marriage on that account. The two lovers discussed the obstacle. There appeared to be no way for Juan to capitalize on his training and talents without going to Italy and to this Iñes objected as there were too many beautiful girls in Italy.

However, there was America. It still was an enchanted land. There were recurrent stories of large fortunes being made almost over night in the provinces of New Spain and in the golden dreams of youth all things are possible.

Juan swallowed his pride. It was hard for him to lay aside his ambitious visions and become a mere gold-seeker. But his love for Iñes dominated every other consideration and he yielded, making his plans to come to America. Texas at that time was a promising region for there were stories current of a *gran quivira* [41] – a great treasure of gold and silver – to be found somewhere in the unexplored parts of that province.

In 1720 Huisar arrived at Bexar – now a part of San Antonio, Texas. There he began laying plans to conduct a small expedition northwestward in search of the *gran quivira,* which indian legend stated lay in that direction.

But he did not make the journey. A ship from Spain reached Matagorda Bay, bearing some supplies for the Bexar presidio and the missions of that district. It also carried a message for Juan Huisar.

The king of Spain desired to revive and foster the art of the kingdom which had declined since the death of Murillo, Velasquez, and their contemporaries. He had learned that the talented young sculptor, Juan Huisar, had left Spain, and he desired to keep such men at home. So the message that now was delivered to Juan was the offer of a large annuity on the condition that he return to Spain and devote himself to his chosen work.

Juan was overjoyed. A liberal income, an opportunity to do his chosen work, and Iñes. In his most gorgeous dreams he had never pictured for himself such good fortune.

He was informed that within four months another ship would touch at Matagorda Bay and would sail thence to Spain. So during four slow-dragging months Juan gave himself up to roseate dreams and prayed for fair winds and smooth seas. When, at the end of that

---

[41] See "The gran quivira" legend.

time, the expected ship pricked through the haze of
Cavallo pass, Juan was there to meet it. He had left
Bexar some days before and had gone to stay at the
Bahia mission, near Matagorda Bay.

A boat put off from the ship and rowed to the shore.
It carried an officer of the ship, Alonso Gardenas, who
was an old-time friend of Huisar's.

Gardenas was surprised to see Juan, for he had expected to find him at Bexar. The two young men met
with ardent demonstrations of friendship, and Gardenas
heartily congratulated Juan upon the favor that the
king had extended him.

But Juan detected some restraint in his friend's be-
havior, and finally questioned him.

"Well, Juan," answered Gardenas, hesitatingly,
"well, I know you would rather hear of it from me than
from a stranger, but the truth is — Juan, the Señorita
Iñes — well, your former fiancée is married."

Juan blanched underneath his tan staring dazedly at
Gardenas, whose eyes moistened in sympathy with the
sudden agony of his friend. Then, holding Juan by the
arm, Gardenas walked him up and down the beach.

"It is well. It is very well," came hoarsely from Juan's
lips. Presently he stopped.

"Leave me, Alonso," he said. "I want to be alone."

Gardenas, respecting the man's grief, silently returned to his boat and was rowed back to his ship.

For a long time the stricken man stood motionless on
the sands. Then he started slowly on his way back to
the mission.

There he unburdened his heart to the fatherly old
priest, who listened without comment until the young
man had finished his broken tale.

"Women are much alike, Juan," he said, gently, "whether noble or common, as I myself once learned to my sorrow." He laid a kindly hand on Juan's shoulder. "An old man who in his youth drank the same cup sympathizes with you, my son.

"But work is the best nepenthe for sorrow, Juan," he continued, "and we have work for you to do. Thank God's mercy for that. The erection of the mission San José has been started near Bexar, and an artist of your talent is needed to execute the decorations. Go there, my son, and dedicate your life and your talents to God. Forget your pain in your work."

The next morning Huisar departed, alone and desolate, for the San José mission. Arrived there he offered his services to those who were superintending the erection of the church. They accepted him with rejoicing. A few days later he began his work.

The rest of his story can be briefly told. He spent eleven years on the sculptures of the San José and during this time he became transformed into a gloomy old man. He lived solitarily and had little contact with his fellows. From morning to night, every day except sundays, his mallet and chisel were busy on the white stone. It is said that he endeavored to convey his deep sense of tragedy and despair in the wonderful carvings of the façade and baptistry window of that splendid edifice.

At the end of this long task he sent a simple message to the now aged priest at Bahia: "Work has not eased my pain, Father." Shortly thereafter he was found dead in his cabin and was buried in the shadow of the San José which for two centuries was his only monument.

Huisar's work marks him as a sculptor of the first

Façade of the San José

rank. No qualified judge ever has stated otherwise. Even today, battered by the elements and defaced by the vandal and with the delicate tracery nearly obliterated by two centuries of weathering, the sculptures of the San José are studied by artists from all parts of the civilized world. The Texas historian, William Corner, has this to say of these masterpieces:

The hand that chiseled the wonderful façade at the main entrance of the church, the doorway, the window and pillar capitals of the smaller chapel, was one of marvelous cunning. The façade is rich to repletion with the most exquisite carving. Figures of saints and virgins, with drapery that looks like drapery, cherubs, heads, ornate pedestals and recesses with their conch-like canopies, and cornices wonderful. . .

The south window of the baptistry is considered by good judges to be the finest gem of architectural ornamentation in America today. . . . It is the kind of art that does not satiate, but ever reveals some fresh beauty in line or curve.

Just how much truth there is in the story of Huisar's love affair can not be learned. Various versions of the legend differ considerably in detail. This much, it appears, the historian will concede: that Huisar came to Texas a buoyant young man; that some news he received from Spain affected him profoundly and caused him to remain in Texas; that he undertook the sculptural decoration of the San José and worked thereon from about 1720 to 1731; that he aged rapidly during that time and died shortly after he had finished his work.

The tradition (which is mentioned in but one version of the legend) that he was a descendant of the creator of the Alhambra has been doubted because Huisar was a Spaniard and not a Moor. The present writers share those doubts; nevertheless the name (also spelled Huicar) is moorish and not Spanish. The christianized

Moors never were expelled from Spain. One of the first four men to tread the soil of our southwest was a Moor, although a subject of the crown of Spain.

On the occasion of our last visit to the San José mission in 1933 we found that since our last preceding visit an appropriate monument of white marble had been erected at the head of Huisar's grave, and that the entire original mission of San José was being reconstructed in miniature on a scale estimated to be one-eighth on the grounds of that historic institution. The work, even to the reproduction of Huisar's delicate tracery, was being executed with absolute fidelity and the visitor to the San José now may obtain some appreciation of the beauty of Huisar's sculptures as they were two centuries ago.

Bells of the San José

Some time during the period of 1720 to 1731 there arrived at the Bexar presidio a young soldier named Carlos de Leon.[42]

Carlos had chosen a military career and had enlisted in the royal army as a private. Desiring both military experience and an officer's commission, he had sought and obtained assignment to a presidio on the Texas frontier.

The young Carlos de Leon possessed an incentive for seeking reputation and military rank. In Xeres, Spain, he had left his fiancée, Teresa. As a private, his wages were not sufficient to support a wife in Spain and he did not wish to subject Teresa to the hardships and dangers of life on a new frontier. There was small opportunity for advancement in Spain, but the New World offered liberal promotion to the young soldier who should prove himself on Spain's colonial frontier.

Carlos participated in a number of battles with the Comanches, fights in which he was conspicuous for his daring and enterprise. His subsequent promotion to the rank of lieutenant seemed only to whet his appetite for danger.

He still had about six months of his period of enlistment to serve when the final battle with the Comanches took place. The Indians had collected their whole force of warriors into one army, while Governor Bustillos

---

[42] One version of the legend gives this man's name as Angel de Leon. But Angel de Leon still was living in San Fernando in 1762.

had drawn upon every presidio along the Rio Grande for troops to meet this formidable array of savages.

Before the Spanish troops set out from Bexar, Bustillos handed Carlos a document. It was a promotion signed by the viceroy, the Marqués de Casa-Fuerte, giving Carlos the rank and salary of a captain of the royal cavalry.

Carlos was overjoyed. He now was in a position to marry Teresa. The fact that he had several times been wounded in action entitled him to a post in Spain or in one of the well-settled provinces of Spain's overseas empire. The command of a presidio now was easily within his reach. Possibly one day he would be appointed governor of a province.

The two armies, Spaniards and Indians, met some 30 miles northwest of Bexar late in the evening. Neither side attacked that night; the Spaniards were unfamiliar with the ground, while the savages were superstitious about night fighting.

The next morning the Spanish cavalry advanced in a wedge-shaped formation, Carlos leading at the point of the wedge. This formation moved at a trot until within a short distance of the howling savages and then, at a word of command from Carlos, it broke into a hard gallop and struck.

The rushing wedge drove far into the dense array of Indians before its momentum was checked. Carlos's impetuosity carried him forward and separated him from his fellows; then the rising clouds of dust hid him from view.

The Indians finally were overwhelmed and scattered. Now, as the weary and begrimed cavalrymen reassembled, it was found that Carlos was missing.

Direct sailings of ships to Matagorda Bay had been instituted in 1720, although the voyages were far apart. Teresa, back in old Xeres, knew that the first of these ships to return to Spain would bring a letter from Carlos.

And so it did bring her a message from her Carlos — a pathetic little farewell note, scrawled in agony as he lay dying in the mission of San José. It was accompanied by a letter from the *padre superior* of the mission, telling her how Carlos was found shot through by two arrows; how he was carried 30 miles to the mission; how they strove to save his life; how he died and was buried in the *campo santo* of the San José.

Teresa collapsed, and for many days hovered between life and death.

Then came the announcement that the bells intended for the new mission in Texas (the San José) were presently to be cast.

When Teresa heard of it, she asked that she be taken to the scene, and after some expostulation her wish was granted. A large concourse of people already had gathered when Teresa arrived for the casting of mission bells always was a ceremony, witnessed by a large crowd of people who gathered to celebrate the event. In response to Teresa's request, she was taken through the crowd to where the moulds had been prepared for the pouring, while the bell-metal itself, shimmering with heat in its great fire-clay caldron, was all ready for the casting.

Teresa slowly arose and removed the gold ring and crucifix that Carlos had given her before departing for Texas. Raising these in her hand, she cast them into the molten metal, crying,

"O bells, take these with you, and when for the first time you ring the Angelus above his grave, he will hear, and will understand, and will know that I have been faithful."

She sank in a faint and was carried away.

Thereafter Teresa declined in health, until her hold on life was fragile indeed. She had no desire to recover, yet for some reason she clung desperately to life, day after day, as though waiting and hoping for some news or for some event.

Then, one weary night, as her parents were watching beside her bed, her thin face suddenly became glorified by a beautiful smile, and raising herself as her mother sprang to her side:

"The Angelus!" she whispered. "They are ringing the Angelus, and Carlos hears – and understands!"

Then she died, her face still transfigured by that wonderful smile.

It afterward was learned that at the very hour Teresa died, the Angelus was being sounded for the first time on the chimes of the San José in far-away Texas.

———

The preceding legend also is related of the San Gabriel mission in California. But we find that of the three bells in the San Gabriel, one was cast in Massachusetts in 1828, another in San Francisco in 1830, and the other in 1795 – place not known, but evidently of Mexican manufacture.

The bells of the San José, of which but one now remains, unquestionably were cast in Spain prior to 1631, for there is a record of their transportation to Texas. The legend itself was known in Texas at least one and one-half centuries ago.

Antonia's Leap

In the valley of the Colorado river in Texas is a nearly sheer precipice, as though a great hill had been sliced vertically and the one half removed. It now is known as Mount Bonnell, but the earliest Anglo-american settlers knew of it as Antonette's leap. This name doubtless is a corruption of the Spanish name Antonia, for there is no such word in Spanish as Antonette, and the legend is of Spanish origin. It is widely known in Texas, and several variants have sprung from it and attached themselves to this and other precipices in the state. – C.H.

One morning about the year 1735, at the villa of San Fernando, there was gathered at the site where their new church was being erected a group of the colonists, idly discussing the progress that was being made in the erection of the building.[43] Among them was Navarro, the young architect who had planned the church.

Now, from a distance, but sounding clear above the chatter, there came through the air the full, sweet notes of a mocking-bird. A moment later the small assemblage was startled to hear from their midst a repetition of the strain. Then, understanding, all eyes turned with amusement to Navarro. On each of that young man's cheeks a dull red pushed through his heavy coat of tan.

---

[43] Different writers place the building of the San Fernando church between 1731 and 1739. There was a small church erected in 1731, another three or four years later, and a third, the existing one, in 1739.

Then, abruptly turning, he went to meet the girl who was coming toward him from the near-by settlement. His answer to her mocking-bird call had been so quick and ardent that he felt somewhat abashed by the smiles and looks of amused tolerance from the onlookers.

Antonia had been with the expedition of colonists who had come to Texas from the Canary islands and had founded San Fernando in 1731. Antonia and Navarro were betrothed, and for some time Navarro had been doing double duty supervising the erection of the church and of his own future home.

As the two walked on slowly toward Antonia's home in the northwestern part of the settlement, neither observed that they were being followed by two Indians. The Indians of the Valero mission were continually hanging around the Spanish settlements of San Fernando and Bexar, and, being well-behaved, were unobjectionable.

Upon leaving Antonia's door, Navarro encountered these two who respectfully stepped out of the pathway and saluted him as he passed. He recognized them as two Comanche neophytes of the Valero mission. These two Comanches had come to the Valero less than a month before, and had asked admission to that celebrated indian industrial school. They proved so faithful and obedient that after two or three weeks they were given the liberty of the settlements, although, of course, they were required to return to their quarters in the mission courtyard each night.

On the evening after they had trailed Navarro and Antonia to her home these two Indians did not return to the mission. The padres were vexed, but gave little more thought to the matter, for occasionally a native gave way to his savage nature and deserted, rejoining his tribe on the plains of Texas.

Three days later was sunday. The quiet of a perfect spring morning lay like the peace of God upon the little community. Along the narrow San Antonio river the cluster of angular presidio buildings lay sleeping in the sun, a lone sentry pacing lazily back and forth. People by pairs and families were sauntering to mass in the improvised church that was serving their spiritual needs temporarily, while from four miles down the valley came on the quiet air the chimes of the San José, calling its indian congregation to worship.

Suddenly there came a clatter of horses' hoofs on a hard gallop, and a cloud of dust began rising from the edge of the settlement. Then the riders were seen – a score of half-naked Comanches! Shouts of terrified warning mingled with the thudding of hoofs; then came two stabbing, agonized screams of horror as the Comanche band, sweeping past Antonia's home, tore her from her mother's arms and swung her up on the horse ridden by the chief!

It was like the rushing swoop of a hawk. The alarm bell rang out and the small garrison at the presidio came forth in haste; but pursuit was useless – they could not overtake the abductors, and they were too few in number to attack a whole Comanche village.

But Navarro, crazed by his loss and rendered unreasonable with rage, tore away from his friends and rushed to his stable where his faithful Tonkawan servant, anticipating his action, had two swift horses ready.

"I ride with you," he calmly informed Navarro.

"No, Pico! I must go alone! You will stay and take care of my mother if I do not return – I charge you!"

"Then be with God, Señor!" the Indian exclaimed, as Navarro dashed out of the stable-yard. Pico looked steadily after the disappearing rider.

"Si," he said, softly, "si, it is as a man should do."

All through that day Navarro rode, and into the night. His horse, of that andalusian breed that will die before it will be conquered, held its pace, knowing as a horse always knows, that its master was in desperate haste.

Finally, through the darkness, Navarro saw the gleams of the campfires in the Comanche town; and a little later the outlines of the lodges, picked out by the firelights, became distinguishable.

Well outside the village, Navarro picketed his horse and stole cautiously forward on foot. At the outskirts of the encampment he halted, at a loss to know how to proceed. Away in a broad open space surrounded by the straggling ring of lodges, was almost the entire populace of the village, sitting about their campfires, entirely off their guard.

Then the notes of a distant mocking-bird came to Navarro's ears, and it gave him a sudden inspiration. From his lips came the clear, liquid notes:

"Chi'-r-r-r-eé, chi'-r-r-r-eé, chi'-r-r-r-eé, tee'-r-r-r, tee'-r-r-r, tee'-r-r-r."

He waited a moment. No reply came .

He repeated the call, a trifle more loudly.

This time there came an answering trill from some point on the other side of the ring of lodges. Navarro crept softly around, hoping that Antonia would keep repeating the cadence.

And so she did. Every few moments there would come to his ears the rippling notes. Once he replied, to inform her that he was approaching.

Navarro presently identified the lodge from which the call was coming. It was near the outskirts of the village.

He glided up steathily, every sense keenly alert, and in moving around to the entrance of the lodge he saw, guarding the doorway, a squatting Indian with his head bent somnolently forward. At that moment a stick cracked under Navarro's foot and the Indian was instantly on his feet. But he was too late, for Navarro was upon him like a tiger, his fingers closed in a steely grip upon the Indian's windpipe, and the savage went down in a silent struggle for his life.

After a while Navarro rose, but the Indian remained lying in a contorted position upon the ground.

Navarro found Antonia lashed fast to the centerpole of the wigwam, bound with rawhide thongs. He quickly cut these and the two of them crept directly out of the encampment, then circled around to where his horse was waiting. Swinging Antonia up behind him, Navarro made a wide detour and struck directly southwestward toward San Fernando instead of taking the trail southward for the double purpose of making his trail harder to follow and to shorten the distance to the settlement.

But when morning dawned with a cloudy sky the two discovered that they had become lost in the labyrinthine hills of the Colorado, and they had no sun to guide them. All that day and the following night they struggled through the boulder-strewn canyons.

On the second morning they saw in the far distance the telltale cloud of dust that informed them the Indians were riding on their trail.

Navarro, believing that he could travel faster on a ridge than through the canyons, urged his tired horse up a long, rising slope of ground before him. But his faithful mount was rapidly weakening, although still bravely struggling forward, while Navarro knew that the Indians, who were plentifully supplied with horses, were on fresh mounts.

By the time the crest of the slope was reached, the foremost of the Indians were riding through the bushes at the bottom. Then Navarro discovered, with a gasp of horror, that the ridge terminated in an abrupt precipice. They were trapped!

He turned and pressed one kiss upon Antonia's cold forehead. Then they dismounted.

The approaching savages, seeing that Navarro carried no visible arms, also dismounted and came forward to capture him alive in order that they might later enjoy torturing him to death in the presence of Antonia.

Navarro suddenly whipped out a pistol and fired, the ball striking the chief squarely in the forehead, and the chief, with a terrible howl, collapsed. But the next instant Navarro went down, shot through by arrows.

Antonia, with magnificent courage, knelt beside her dying lover and pressed her lips to his. Then, eluding the Indians who sprang forward to seize her, she flung herself over the precipice and was crushed on the rocks below.

The Indians paid dearly for this double sacrifice for that same year the grizzled, battle-scarred, old Manuel de Sandoval, with a force recruited from the presidios of Texas and Coahuila, led an expedition against the Comanches and wiped out every village in the region. So bloody was the reprisal taken that it struck fear into every indian tribe for 500 miles around, and for many years the Spaniards in Texas enjoyed peace.

Francesca and Ferenor

On a dismal night in late autumn 26 years ago, I was driving out to the ruins of the old army post of Fort Stockton, of which, except for one or two buildings within the city limits of modern Fort Stockton, only a few broken walls remained. Beside me in my car was an intelligent young Mexican.

I had approached five before finding one willing to accompany me to the old ruins. Four times in succession I had met a polite but firm "No, Señor!" and an expressive shrug of the shoulders.

I knew why they had refused to accompany me, but I wanted to hear the story from the lips of a Mexican. Those people are natural story-tellers, with a keen appreciation of dramatic values. And to hear the tale in its proper setting was the real object of my nocturnal excursion.

So now, as we swung over the dusty wagon road toward the ruins, I turned innocently to my companion with:

"Manuel, why did those other young men refuse to come with me?"

He looked at me quickly. Then:

"Is it possible, Señor, that you know not?" he asked. "You do not?"

"Those hombres had fear, Señor. Yes. It is a story that has been told over and over at our firesides for so many years. If you wish – or is it your wish that I shall tell you the story?"

He deftly rolled and lighted a brown cigarette, and inhaled deeply. Then:

"You have no sweetheart, Señor?" he asked me deferentially.

I assured him that that good fortune was denied me.

"*Bien.* It is very well. No more have I. Therefore, as you see, I accompany you."

He gazed abstractedly into the thick darkness for a few seconds. Then came the story that I was waiting for.

"Señor, where the ruins of old Fort Stockton now stand, there was, in the early days, a Spanish presidio. You comprehend presidio? It was a community military — soldiers and their officers and families and a few *colonos* — ah, colonists.

"The name of this old establishment has not come down to us, but it may have been the *presidio de Pena Colorado*. A name abhorrent, is it not, Señor? 'the presidio of red suffering!' [44]

"In the early Spanish days — it must have been near to the year of 1750 — there lived in this *presidial* community a young priest named Ferenor. That is, he was preparing for the holy calling under the instruction of his uncle, the padre, who was in charge of the community church and who lived alone in his convento apart from the settlement. This old padre possessed great pride of his nephew, who indeed was a young man of many perfections, and it was his desire that Ferenor succeed him as padre of the presidio church.

"Ferenor already had taken the *voto de celibato* — the vow that barred him from marriage — although he

---

[44] Manuel was in error here. The name is *Peña Colorado*. *Pena* means suffering, but *peña* means stone or rock, and had reference to the red sandstone that abounds in many districts of western Texas.

had not yet taken upon himself the final vows binding him to the holy church.

"Then, as *el diablo* would have it, Ferenor met and fell in love with the Señorita Francesca. But no. I shall not say 'as the devil would have it.' Ferenor was a man, and Francesca was *muy bonita* – very lovely. And what are a man's strongest vows when opposed to the fires of love? Little sticks, Señor, that are consumed to ashes. Ah – you never have loved, nor have I, *pero comprendemos,* Señor, we can understand – we can understand.

"But Ferenor fought, too, against this love that had come to him. *De verdad,* he resisted! And all to no avail. In the swelling choruses in the church, he could hear naught but Francesca's thrilling notes. The deep *azul* of the autumn sky was to him only the color of her eyes. In the *santissima* face of the Holy Mary he saw only a reflection of his earthly saint. There was room in his mind for but one thought and in his heart for but one image – the *bonita* Francesca. You Americans, Señor, I believe say the same thing, and with no doubt more beautifully, in your expression, 'He felled for her, by heck.'

"And because of this love, the renunciation of his holy vows, so sacrilegious at first to his mind, became a determination with Ferenor. Yes, in truth his vows became hateful to him, and he renounced them with bitterness, knowing that this *apostasia* would bring both sorrow and wrath to his beloved uncle, the padre.

"Now the Señorita Francesca had suitors a plenty; and all of them young men very *excelente,* if we except the Indian, Ytur Yupiha, truly a black coyote, as the name signifies; although when he accepted baptism and came to live with the other christian Indians at the presidio, he was rechristened Pablo by the priest. I shall call him Ytur, for in truth his soul was that of a black coyote. He, although he had been a chief in his own country, was a liar and a *ladron,* and his christianity was of a vile pretension.

"Imagine, Señor, an Indian — even a chief — having aspiration to marry a white girl *muy alto — tan caro —* so high above him that she was as a star in the heavens and he as but of the earth a clod! *Pero,* he did not consider that, but believed himself to be under the favor of the christian and savage gods alike.

"And Francesca, with the unreason that ever abides in her sex — as you and I know, Señor — she loved only Ferenor, even though knowing that his vows forbade marriage. Si, she loved a priest, or one who was near to becoming a priest.

"Now on a dark evening, such a one as is this evening — a *noche triste,* in fact — Ferenor and Francesca went together, as was their custom, to the vesper services in the church, and as they walked from the *colonia* toward the church they were silent. For they had made the determination to ask Ferenor's uncle, the padre, to unite them in marriage on that evening; and in consequence of this determination, they possessed that strange shyness and *timidez* that falls upon lovers approaching their marriage.

"It seemed to the two lovers that the padre made a sermon of great length that evening; but after the *congregación* had been dismissed and all the other people had departed to their homes, the two sought the padre in his garden. He was not to be found there, so they returned again to the church; but it was all in darkness and was deserted except for a dim figure that was lurking in the shadows under the *portales*. When Ferenor approached this figure, thinking of a possibility it might be his uncle, the padre, it glided away into the blackness of the night.

"The pair at last found the padre in a room of the convento. He arose from his chair with surprise as they entered, and then a dark frown of disapprobation came over his face.

" 'Father,' began Ferenor, with apprehension, 'we have come to you with the desire that you unite us together in marriage.' He could say no more because of the stern look in his uncle's eyes, but he drew Francesca up to him and enfolded an arm about her.

"The priest regarded his nephew with anger and scorn, and for a while he made no talk. A younger man – si, even you or I, Señor – would have relented because of the pleading light in Francesca's eyes. But the priest was an old man, and Ferenor was his only kindred, so let us have charity.

"So the padre now spoke with contempt on his tongue:

" 'You would renounce riches divine for pleasures of the earth, Ferenor? You would break holy vows, and thereby blaspheme His Holy Name? You would do this? Maledictions upon you! You shall not! Ferenor, never will I lend my aid or my sanction to such sacrilege!'

"The two lovers were wounded by these words, and for a moment they were silent and spoke to each other only with their eyes. Then Ferenor found his voice and spoke like a man of resolution, calling to his uncle's mind that other priests in the past had made renunciation of their vows and had married and that no vengeance of heaven was visited upon them in consequence thereof, and that he refused, *absolutamente,* to be further bound by vows that he had taken upon himself without thought at his uncle's urging.

"But as Ferenor valiantly argued, the old padre grew more angry, and then *furioso,* and at the last, he commanded them to depart on the instant from the convento, threatening them with excommunication if they spoke further.

"Ah, *fue malo.* But he was an old man – very old.

"Francesca clung to Ferenor as they stumbled into the night, for she could not see because of the hot tears that the old priest had brought from her eyes.

"A thick fog had come down over the land while they were in the convento, and because of this, together with their pain and humiliation, the lovers strayed from the pathway leading back to the *colonia* without becoming aware of it. But after a while, they recognized that the ground had become rough under their feet, and no lights shone through the thick night to guide them; neither were there any stars. They could see nothing, for the blackness was *absoluto.*

"They made haste on in the direction in which they believed the *colonia* to lay, but as they went on and on and no cabins came into their view, they turned about and made effort to go back over their trail, but this confused them the more. Had they possessed their senses, they now would have stopped and waited for the day; but both were stricken with grief and humiliation, and knew not what they did.

"So they continued to wander for hours, until at last Francesca became so wearied that she was not able to walk farther, and she sank to the ground.

"At that moment Ferenor gave a glad shout, for his eye had caught sight of a light shining dimly through the fog. He pointed it out to Francesca and she also now was gladdened. Ferenor could not know how far it was; it might be only a few *varas,* or it might be half a league. So he wrapped his *capa* about Francesca to keep her warm and then hurried on toward the light to get help and go back for Francesca.

"But for some cause he could not reach that light. On and on he pursued it, thinking that by running he could come up with the person carrying it. Then, when he had become quite out of breath and ready to fall to the ground from his extreme weariness, the light all at once disappeared.

"Ferenor stopped. Walls of blackness closed him in. He now believed that the light he had followed was either a witch-light or else was a torch carried by some one desiring to mislead him. He was filled with alarm.

"So he made haste to return to Francesca. That is to say, he thought he was going back to her, but his steps led him into hills that he had not encountered before.

"Now he began running frantically here and there, calling,

" 'Francesca! FRANCESCA! FRANCESCA!'

"But as no answer came to his ears, however loudly he called, he became more and more alarmed, and after a while he stumbled and fell, striking his head on a stone, and knew no more.

"When consciousness at last returned to him, the dawn had come, and the fog had gone; and far away, but in a direction opposite to what he had believed, he saw the *torreon* of the church, with gilded cross shining in the light of the rising sun.

"He came at once to his feet, and looked about for Francesca, and sought for her, and from every hilltop thereabouts he called aloud to her. But all to no good.

"Then it came to him that she had made her way back alone to the *colonia,* and so, relieved in mind, he hurried his steps thereto. But when he arrived, he found the people there seeking both himself and Francesca, and he became much alarmed. He told as well as he could of what had happened in the night, and how he had been led away from Francesca by the strange light.

"The most skilled trackers among the Indians were then called together, and then it was found that Ytur also had disappeared in the night.

"Upon this Ferenor became loco, and was not to be controlled. Against the will of his friends he saddled his horse to set out for the indian village, far away, from which Ytur had come.

"So Ferenor spurred away in great haste, and disappeared from view in the hills to the northward.

"And, Señor, that was the last that was seen of Ferenor forever, nor was he heard of any more.

"The next day a company of men from the presidio departed for that same indian village. But upon reaching it, the Indians there made profound assurance that they had seen nothing of Francesca, Ferenor, or Ytur. A search of their village availed nothing. So no more could be done.

"Many months later there came a story, or — what do you call it, a rumor? — that a girl like Francesca had been seen with that tribe. But so vigilante were those Indians that the Spaniards never were able to steal upon their village without being seen afar off; and after a time that tribe, fearing the *animosidad* of the Spaniards, removed to a more distant region.

"And so it was that Francesca and Ferenor came to grief, Señor.

"They after a time ceased to be in the thoughts of their people, but their story has come down through the years to us. Some declare that the fate of the two lovers was a *retribución* sent by God for their having dared to love, but I can not think so, Señor — assuredly I can not think so — nor can I believe that you would think so. No? *Esta buena;* you believe rightly.

"The old Spanish settlement itself is but a memory today, Señor, and the army post that the Americans erected on the site a century after is now itself but a heap of old ruins. As you shall see for yourself, for we shall be there presently.

"The fear that is held of those ruins? Señor, some of those crumbling walls are the remains of the Spanish presidio, the church, and the convento.

"And on dark nights, such as is tonight, the voice of Ferenor is heard, first here and then there, about the old walls, crying, now in a wail and now in a sigh,

" 'Francesca! FRANCESCA! FRANCESCA!'

"But, call as he may through the night, there comes no answer to his cry save the sighing and sobbing of the wind through the *chapparal*.

"And whenever a lover hears this cry, it portends grief or *dolar* to him or his *enamorita* — his sweetheart — and, Señor, most of the young men have sweethearts. So it is that they will not approach these ruins at night, nor will they come near them in the day if they can avoid it.

"But you and I, Señor – we have none dear to us, and so, even though the ghostly call of Ferenor comes to us on the night wind, we shall have no fear.

"Stop immediately ahead, Señor; you can go no farther with your car. The black wall just before us is of the old convento."

No wail of anguished lover met our ears while we were exploring the desolate ruins. From the blackness overhead came the occasional flutter of bat wings, and from around us the rustle of unseen lizards and sand-scorpions scurrying from the light of our gasoline lantern.

Those, and the eerie night breeze moaning a *miserere* through the crumbling old walls.

We find no historical evidence that there ever was a Spanish settlement on or near the present site of Fort Stockton, although it is possible. Had there been a presidio there, there surely would be documentary evidence of it. Civilian settlements often had a militia company and a sort of barracks, and possibly this is what Manuel had in mind when he referred to a presidio.

However, the writers are inclined to believe that the incidents of this legend, if true, occurred at either San Saba or San Luis Amarillas, both west Texas settlements and both having presidios, and that the legend, like several others of the southwest, has been transplanted.

A Legend of Baffle Point

The old sea captain, Almonte, was 63, irascible and wealthy when he gave up the sea and came with his daughter Luisa to East Bay on the coast of Texas. Finding the coastal climate of that district more to his liking than that of old Spain, he decided to spend his remaining days there.

He secured a beautiful estate overlooking the bay to the east, and there, on a low hill rising from the beach, he built a large, one-story stone house after the moorish pattern, with an inclosed court. On the south side of this home was his apartment, with its long, low windows commanding a wide sweep of the gulf.

About 200 yards below his house he had his own wharf of solid masonry, for, while he had given up the seas, he still possessed a beautiful yacht, constructed after his own designs, and in this he often took pleasure trips up and down the coast. His daughter Luisa herself was an expert sailor of small craft and, as she loved the open water as much as did her father, she accompanied him on these trips at every opportunity.

Old Almonte entertained a contempt, amounting almost to hatred, for all fishermen. He would have hated them had he not considered them too far below his station. During his years as a deep-water navigator in the Royal Marine, he had experienced much trouble with the fisher folk. When near land, their sloops continually were getting in the way of the proud square-rigger that he captained, and these ubiquitous little craft also arrogantly interfered with the maneuvers of his ship when tacking into or out of a land-locked harbor. Indeed, once in a sudden rage he had driven his ship over a fishing sloop that he thought was too tardy in obeying his profane orders to it to clear out, a hot-headed act that won for Almonte a humiliating reprimand from the commandant of the port.

Many fishermen lived around East Bay, but from them Almonte held proudly aloof. He had not dreamed that Luisa, with the blood of fine old castilian families in her veins, ever would condescend even to recognize the existence of such lowly people. Consequently, he was both astounded and angry when Luisa began associating with a young fisherman named Alvarez. It enraged him to think of Alvarez, possessing no property except his little cabin and his boat, aspiring to equality with Luisa Almonte.

He summoned the girl to his apartment and severely lectured her, telling her plainly that he would have none of the young man in his family and ordering her to ignore Alvarez in the future.

"There is young Castillo," he reminded her insinuatingly, "whose father's hacienda is next to mine. Castillo will come into all his father's wealth one of these days, and he is of one of the oldest families of Barcelona."

"But, *padre mío,*" objected Luisa, "Don Castillo gets drunk, and gambles, and never a week goes by that he does not have a fight with some one."

"That is just the natural exuberance of youth. He will settle down after a while. That fishmonger of yours hasn't spirit enough to fight or get drunk."

A hot retort rose to Luisa's lips, but remembering

her father's violent temper she checked it; and the conference ended with her dutifully promising never to permit Alvarez to come upon her father's land again. And Almonte knew that his daughter kept her word.

Some days later, on a beautiful moonlit evening, such as can be seen nowhere else in the world except on the gulf coast, Almonte was minded to go for a little sail in his yacht. A fresh, cool breeze, that would make a sail delightfully exhilarating, was springing up. He supposed that Luisa would want to go with him.

But the servant, sent to inquire her pleasure, returned with the information that Luisa was neither in her apartment nor in the court, and further, that her best mantilla was missing. Almonte assumed that she had gone for a stroll on the beach, as she often had done, so he went on alone down to the shore expecting to find her there. Several fishing sloops were anchored between the pathway and Almonte's pier, and there in one of them were Luisa and Alvarez, his arm around her shoulders, watching the moon climb up over the bay. The sand had muffled Almonte's footsteps, and his approach had not been observed by the pair of lovers.

Old Almonte was beside himself with rage, and but for Luisa's interference, he would have killed Alvarez then and there. He ordered Luisa ashore and as Alvarez moved to assist her out of the boat, Almonte blazed,

"Keep your hands off her, cur!" and helped her ashore himself. Alvarez's face went white in the moonlight, but he said nothing.

Almonte turned to him. "Don't let me lay eyes on you again, or you are dead! There are to be no fishmongers in my family!"

Alvarez's eyes blazed at the insult, but a warning

sign from Luisa checked him, and he bowed deeply to old Almonte, sweeping the ground with his hat.

"It is well," he answered. "You shall see no more of me forever."

He turned about and departed toward his little cabin around the arm of the bay, without once looking back. Almonte's eyes followed him contemptuously.

"Any man of courage," he remarked sneeringly to Luisa, "would have fought to the death at that insult. He walked away, cowed."

Luisa made no reply.

"And you, Señorita," he cried, his anger again mounting, "remember that you have done a thing that no one of my family – no Almonte – ever has done before! You have broken your word!"

"I have not done so!" retorted Luisa. "Señor Alvarez has not set foot on our land since I made my promise to you! He sails across the bay, and I meet him at the beach. He does not leave his boat!"

Ah, the simplicity of the old, the duplicity of the young!

If Almonte had been wise, he would have been put on his guard by the lack of resistance offered by the pair. As it was, he flattered himself that he had nipped the prohibited romance in the bud.

Late that night, Luisa stole down to the bay where Alvarez was waiting, climbed into his sloop, and they sailed across the water to where the priest lived, and the priest joined them in marriage. Then they sailed on out of the bay and southward down the coast, and so disappeared.

In the morning when old Almonte discovered that Luisa had fled, he became infuriated and terrible from rage. He poured out torrents of curses and blasphemy until the very servants, crossing themselves, fled in fright from the house.

But the girl was gone. There was no help for it, and no vengeance that he might presently take. But in his wrath he swore that he would visit his revenge upon other fishermen. He called satan to his aid, and through him caused sandbars to be raised in the water, and sand-hills on the shore to produce dangerous cross-currents in the wind and treacherous whirlpools in the water of that portion of the bay traversed by fishermen.

The diabolic scheme, however, did not have the results that Almonte had desired and anticipated. A number of sailboats were capsized in the whirlpools, but no lives were lost, and the fishermen soon learned to steer clear of the dangerous water and take a roundabout course through the bay.

A year passed. During that time, old Almonte heard no word of his daughter and he was too proud to make any inquiries. He often shuddered, however, at the thought that the two foolhardy young people might have been wrecked and drowned in their dash down the coast, for the night they fled was gusty, with choppy seas. Yet, he knew, both were good sailors. If they had stopped at any near-by settlement, he believed that he would have heard of it, although he knew his servants themselves would have feared to speak to him of his runaway daughter and her fisher husband.

The old man's wrath had cooled, too, and he now repented his rage. Loneliness gnawed at his heart. His luxurious home stood empty, desolate, and silent, and in it there was no one who cared for him. His beautiful yacht lay idle, its hull over-grown with seaweed.

He knew that Luisa loved her father. She had not fled from him; he had driven her away. He knew that at a word of contrition from him, she and Alvarez would, if living, come gladly back to enliven the gloomy house and brighten his declining years. If living!

His estimate of Alvarez had changed since the suitor he had favored for his daughter, Don Castillo, had been banished from the country with an indelible stain upon his name. Almonte shuddered at thought of what Luisa's lot would have been as the wife of Castillo. Alvarez was, at least, a man of honor and uprightness, and his poverty now seemed insignificant by comparison with the other man's degeneracy.

Yet, though his rage had cooled and his resentment had died, the old man's obstinate pride was not broken. He longed for Luisa as only a lonely, broken parent can long for the return of a loved child; but he fought down every impulse to have her sought for.

He missed her in the mornings, for she herself always used to bring him his morning cup of chocolate. He missed her in his now solitary walks along the beach. He had discontinued his recreational sails and his attendance upon mass, for at such times Luisa had been his companion; and now her absence on such occasions would make his loss more poignantly felt.

After a time, this brooding and remorse began to undermine his health, which declined until he was too weak to leave the house and its secluded court. Then, finally, his increasing weakness confined him to his apartment and he came to realize that unless his misery of loneliness and repentance were relieved, he had not long to live.

So his fierce pride was conquered at last. He caused

the message to be spread all up and down the coast, and inland as far as settlements reached, clear to the Grande river, that he desired his daughter and her husband to come home. He allowed no intimation of his illness to go with this appeal, lest Lusia believe that it was this, rather than repentance, that had caused his change of heart.

So humbled was he that he even made confession to the priest, and bared his entire heart, even to telling the priest how, in a dream, he had conversed with satan, and how satan had agreed to bring about the discomfiture of his hereditary enemies.

"That was a grievous sin," declared the priest when the man had finished. "It was a deep sin, and deeply shall you suffer for it; if not in this world, then in the next."

"But is there no pardon?" quavered the old man.

"There can be no pardon for such a sin until expiation be made," answered the priest. "How the expiation will come, it is not given me to see, but my heart pities you for the terrible retribution that sometime shall visit you."

Weary day after day passed, and no word came of those whom Almonte was seeking. It was possible, he reflected, that they had gone so far down the coast that his message would be many days in reaching them. There was a possibility that they had gone far inland, although hardly likely, for Alvarez doubtless would continue his occupation as a fisherman. All the fishermen of Galveston Bay, Matagorda Bay, Corpus Christi Bay, and the long reaches of the Laguna de la Madre had been informed of Almonte's desire. Surely, Luisa and Alvarez would get the message, if living!

After three weeks of waiting, the old man gave up hope, and with the vanishing of hope went also his desire to live. He lay listlessly all day upon his couch by his south window, gazing out over the great expanse of water that he once had proudly sailed as a captain of the Royal Marine. He grew a little weaker, day by day.

Then, one evening just before sunset, when the hills were stretching their shadows across the bay, he saw, through his window, a graceful sailboat rapidly approaching from the south. The wind was brisk and gusty, and even though he was weak and lethargic, the old man admired the skill with which the craft was being handled under a full load of sail.

He gave an involuntary gasp of pleasure at the sight as the boat swung out on a wide tack and then, close-hauling with the lee gunwales awash, rounded about and skimmed like a swallow through the entrance of the bay. It was a masterly maneuver!

Now Almonte sat suddenly upright in bed, startled into wakefulness, for the boat was running straight toward the treacherous whirlpools. A stranger craft, the old man thought, or it would know of and avoid that dangerous water.

Then, as though galvanized into action by some sudden enlightenment, he leaped from his bed with a miraculous accession of strength and rushed from the house, screaming,

"STOP THEM! STOP THEM!"

He raced out into view of the oncoming sloop and frantically waved it to turn – but he received a joyous answering wave from a woman seated at the tiller! His signals had been tragically misunderstood!

The next instant the boat was caught. It plunged forward like a suddenly-roweled horse, hesitated, whirled about as the man on board made a frantic leap with his knife for the halyards, and went over on its side; then a swirl caught its submerged sail and it turned bottom up, circling about in the great whirlpool. Old Almonte, with one hoarse cry of agony, fell forward on his face.

No sailboat dared put out into that water, but a rowboat was hastily manned by the fishermen, who made a desperate effort to reach the capsized craft. They were thrown back again and again by the strong currents, until they were compelled to give up the attempt.

That night the surf washed ashore the bodies of the two victims.

The following day the requiem mass was said over the mortal remains of old Almonte, his daughter Luisa, and his son-in-law, Alvarez. They were buried in one grave, reunited at last.

It is said that the site of this grave is known and is pointed out to curious visitors who have heard the legend.

The building up of the sandbars did not necessitate any supernatural agency, although it is possible that Almonte dreamed that he had an interview with satan. A sandbar can form within a few days. It also is quite possible that the fishermen, who no doubt reciprocated Almonte's hostility, invented the story of his cooperation with the devil, to account for the formation of the dangerous whirlpools.

However, there is no historical evidence of any settlements about Galveston Bay during the Spanish period, and it is the belief of the writers that the true setting of this legend is either Matagorda Bay or Espiritu Santo Bay. – C.H.

Arizona Legends

Arizona Legends

Nearly all the legendary lore of the Spanish period in Arizona has come down to the twentieth century through the Papago and Pima Indians. This we can explain only by the fact that by the year 1820 practically all the people of Spanish blood had been driven out of Arizona by the Apaches, and the settlers who reoccupied the Santa Cruz valley nearly half a century later were not the descendants of the pioneer Spaniards and, therefore knew nothing of the legendary lore of the Spanish period.

Mr. Prent Duell criticises the veracity of the Arizona Indian with the statement that "He is a good story-teller, who does not allow the slender margin of truth to spoil a good story," but we have no evidence that he is more culpable in this respect than is the white man. However, he is likely to interpret as miraculous any occurrence that he can not readily understand or find a simple explanation for. For this reason miraculous occurrences characterize many of the legends that have come down through the Indians.

Of the Arizona legends included herein, that of the San Xavier mission appears to be the only one that is known outside the districts in which their scenes are said to have been enacted. Another rather well-known legend of the San Xavier, "The witchery of Rita," has been preserved, with some accurate character delineation by Will Robinson.

The Girl of Guevavi

Nine miles northeast of Nogales, Arizona, half concealed by the desert growths of sagebrush and mesquite, are a few crumbling walls and mounds of earth – the sole remains of the historic old mission dedicated to the Angels of Guevavi (Los Angeles de Guevavi) founded in 1692.

Father Eusebio Francisco Kino, who established the Guevavi, was born in the Austrian Tyrol in 1644 of German ancestry, "Kino" being the Spanish form of his name, Kuhne. He was a member of the faculty of Ingolstadt university and the companion of princes and nobles. He gave up his work at Ingolstadt at the age of 37 to come to Mexico. In 1683 he began his missionary work in Lower California, and a few years later in Sonora. In all, he founded 27 missions, most of which he stocked with cattle, sheep, and horses from his own ranches.

He lived for nineteen years after founding the Guevavi, and spent a good deal of his time there and at the Tumacacori. The church that figures in the following legend was built in 1701-1702, replacing a smaller structure that had been destroyed by the Apaches, and it was during Kino's last visit to the Guevavi in 1702 that the first incident of this story is supposed to have occurred. Kino mentioned in his journal an incident that doubtless furnished the inspiration for this story. – C.H.

Padre Kino had spent most of the day among the newly-arrived families of Indians, and in the middle of the afternoon he left them, to take a much-needed siesta in the convento before repairing to the church to assist Padre Juan de San Martin with the special vesper services.

He had arrived at Guevavi the day before to dedicate the newly-finished church which, under the direction of Padre San Martin, had been in process of construction for over a year.

The news that Padre Kino was coming brought Indians from half a dozen different rancherias in that region, for they knew and liked him. He had made many tours through their country and had preached to them in their villages. He had baptized some of them. Then, doubtless, the fact that the dedication of his new church would be celebrated by a great feast of roasted and stewed meats, beans, *pinole,* and chocolate, was an added factor in drawing many natives to the scene.

When Padre Kino awoke from his nap, the sun was near to its setting. He rose and after a while moved leisurely toward the church. It wanted two hours before time for the evening services, but he desired to spend this time in prayer at the altar.

As he approached the church, he observed that the native sacristan had left the door wide open. He had instructed him to close and lock it after arranging the altar. But then the Indian had forgotten; he was not used to doors in his mud-walled *jacal.*

Kino paused to survey the edifice. A modest little church it was, being hardly 100 feet long and 40 feet wide; yet it represented many months of hard work on the part of Padre San Martin, aided by two or three Spanish workmen and a few Seri and Pima Indians. In Kino's eyes, its squat tower, little dome, and decorated façade were beautiful.

Now his attention was drawn to something else. Stealing around a corner of the church was a little indian girl, not over six or eight years old. Her eyes were wide with aroused interest and curiosity. Not a detail of the ornamented façade was escaping her notice. It was apparent that she belonged to one of the families who had that day arrived from the lower Santa Cruz valley. It was clear, too, that reconnoitering this building – a magnificent palace and repository of mysteries to her – was a great adventure. Kino stood still and watched.

Satisfied with the exterior, she now stole up to the open door and cautiously peered inside. For a moment she was taken aback by the cavernous interior, and Kino thought she was going to retreat. But her insatiable curiosity got the better of her and, standing in the doorway, she swept her eyes here and there over the great room, into the dark corners, over the ceiling, to the altar and its furnishings.

Seeing nothing fearsome, she stealthily entered, keenly on the alert. After she had passed beyond his vision, Kino softly stole up to the door and peered in. The girl, following along the south wall, was slowly making her way to the altar. The building was but dimly lighted, and the child's whole attention was centered upon the altar and its beautiful furnishings, so that she did not see Kino as he slipped noiselessly in and moved with great circumspection along the dark wall opposite the girl.

Through the one small window south of the altar, the mellow rays of the setting sun poured in and illuminated a life-size statue of the Holy Mother with the infant Christ in her arms. The girl had not yet seen this, it being hidden from her view by the intervening confessional. Kino waited to see what she would do when her slow, cautious progress would bring the statue within her vision, for even to him the images seemed supernaturally beautiful bathed in the gold and orange dyes of sunset.

The child stole around the confessional and then started as from a sudden shock, and a little cry, half of fright and half of adoration, escaped her lips. Her eyes fixed themselves, immovably, upon the beautiful statue. She approached a little closer – then a little closer – never once taking her eyes from the faces of the figures, until she reached the altar rail. Kino approached behind her until he was almost within arm's reach, but for the child nothing at that moment existed in the world except that wonderful mother and infant.

Then, with face uplifted, she extended her arms, half timidly, half eagerly, and began to speak. Kino, who understood her native tongue, leaned forward to catch what she was saying. She was begging for permission to hold the infant!

The calm face of the Mother looked down upon her, but made no reply. Entreatingly, the girl renewed her pleas, her voice now eager, now dying down to a whisper.

Then Kino stepped into view.

"Niña!" he spoke, softly.

Instantly the girl turned with a gasp of fright, her eyes darting about for an avenue of flight. Kino quickly

stepped away, knowing that if she thought herself
trapped she might injure herself trying to escape. Then
the girl, seeing the kindly, smiling face of the old padre,
felt reassured. She had seen this strangely dressed man
before. She had heard her people talk about him, and
knew that they liked him. Only that day she had seen
two wildly delighted indian boys riding behind him
on his horse.

Kino chuckled amusedly as the girl gazed question-
ingly into his face. Then her eyes were drawn again,
irresistibly, to the wonderful statue. Kino addressed
her in her native tongue:

"That is only an image of the Mother and Son whom
I serve, my child," he told her, pointing to the statue.
"It does not live. But the Mother and Babe in whose
likeness this image was made do live, and they are
much more beautiful than their images. Would you
like to see the living Mother and Child some day?"

He had to renew his explanation before he could
make the little girl understand that the statue was not
living, but was made of wood, and that there were a
living Mother and Son whom the statue was used to
represent. He then repeated his question, and the girl
assented, eagerly.

"Then so you shall," he assured her, "if you live
as they desire you to live. I have been sent by them to
teach your people the faith of the true God, so that
some day they shall see and be with the Holy Mother
and her Child."

So talking, he led the way out of the church. It was
quite natural that Kino, animated only by missionary
zeal, should see in this incident only an opportunity
for winning new converts.

So he accompanied the little brown girl to the camp of her parents, and before he left he obtained their consent that not only the girl, but her brothers and sisters, should be baptized and taught the christian faith.

The little girl was baptized the very next day and Kino, following the custom of naming the indian children after the saints, christened this girl Catalina, for she was baptized on Santa Catalina's day.

From that day forth Catalina's dominant desire was to one day see the living Mother and infant Christ. She became Padre San Martin's most obedient and industrious pupil, for Padre Kino had told her, before departing, that if she obeyed her teacher's precepts her wish would sometime be fulfilled.

As she grew older, she began to make herself useful and beloved by her deeds of charity and mercy, and even when only twelve years old, the niña Catalina was esteemed the best nurse in the whole settlement.

When she was fifteen an epidemic struck the settlement and several Indians died. Then the whole community of Indians was thrown into consternation and grief by the news that Catalina, worn out by her unremitting devotion to the needs of others, was herself stricken. Helpless to aid her, dozens of her people sat about, outside the little cabin where she lay sick, praying to both their gods and the god of the christians for her recovery. But she grew steadily worse.

The malady ran a fixed course, and those that died spent their last day in agony. On an evening, it was seen that with Catalina the malady would be fatal, and that the morrow would be her day of torture.

That night, as one of the women of her people watched beside Catalina's bed, the medicine man from

her native village across the mountains entered. For
hours he had been hiding, in the shelter of a deserted
jacal, waiting for an opportunity to steal in to the
sick girl when neither Padre San Martin nor his
brother priest was present.

Catalina recognized him. She knew him to be an
enemy of the christian faith, and she had seen him a
number of times among the neophytes of the mission,
trying to persuade them to return to their native villages and their pagan gods. She knew, too, that this
man hated her for having drawn many of her people
to the mission. As he approached her bedside, after
warning the native attendant to raise no alarm, the
girl shrank from him.

"Have no fear of me," he told her, in his native
tongue, "but listen to what I tell you. Your punishment
shall be more terrible than any I can put upon you,
and it is not far away."

Then he launched forth into a description of the
unspeakable torments to which she would be subjected
after departing this life. She grew terrified, for her
young mind was not entirely weaned from the pagan
superstitions of her tribe.

"Call now upon the god of the white people," the
man advised her, with a hideous leer, "and see if he
can help you! He is a woman-man! You have chosen
to follow his teachings, and now it is too late for you
to make your peace with our gods! Nothing can save
you now! You are doomed!"

Goaded into frenzy, the girl sat up, gasping, hysterically,

"Madre Maria! Madre Maria! Save me!"

At that moment the room became flooded with a soft

radiance, and beside the bed stood the Holy Mother with the infant Christ in her arms!

The girl gasped, and her thin brown face became transfigured. With a wonderful smile, the Mother bent over and, holding out the infant to the girl, placed him in her arms!

The native attendant, who had remained speechless and immovable from terror and amazement, now rushed from the cabin. When she returned with Padre San Martin and others, Catalina was found lying as in a peaceful, refreshing sleep, but lifeless. On the floor lay the body of the medicine man, his unseeing eyes staring with fixed fear, but with no marks upon his body.

The Unfinished Tower of San Xavier

The present church of mission San Xavier del Bac was built during the fourteen years 1783 to 1797. It is the most beautiful specimen of mission architecture to be found on this continent. The gleaming whiteness of the walls and the reddish ornamentation of the façade, with the background of drab desert and cloudless blue sky, make a picture so striking that he who views it never will forget. Mr. Prent Duell, in his *Mission architecture* says:

"San Xavier, in the very heart of the desert, with nothing but sand and sagebrush about, hemmed in by distant mountains, has always attracted artists and students through its very greatness. Travelers who have seen other missions stand amazed before this great, white, isolated cathedral. No mission excels San Xavier in serious design and pure artistry. The two admired towers of Santa Barbara fall far short when compared with those of San Xavier, and the noble dome of the latter has stood unequaled."

A large variety of fruits, vegetables and other crops, grown under irrigation, once supported a considerable indian community at San Xavier.

Many explanations have been advanced for the unfinished state of the right-hand tower of the church. One is that it was not completed for lack of funds. Yet at that time the franciscans had just inherited the large pious fund of the jesuits, and were erecting missions elsewhere and completing them. Eight California missions were completed while the San Xavier was building, and four more were begun in the year when the San Xavier was stopped just short of completion. Then the Tumacacori, only 35 miles from the San Xavier, was begun before work ceased upon the latter, and was completed to the last detail.

Another explanation is that this tower was left without its dome and plaster in imitation of the unfinished condition of many European cathedrals. But no other mission church on this continent was left uncompleted. Some European cathedrals were not finished for the reason that finished churches were taxed, while uncompleted ones were not. But no tax ever was levied on any mission church.

A third theory is that the Ganoa brothers, who made and burned the brick of which the San Xavier is built, died or returned to Spain, and no other brick-makers were available. But this explanation will not hold, either, for we find the Ganoa brothers, a little later, making brick for the Tumacacori, and they would not have been transferred if still needed at the San Xavier.

We can find no historical support for the following legend, but the records of San Xavier since the year 1791 are lost or destroyed, and only fragmentary earlier records of the mission exist. We believe the story to be true in its main incidents. It has been handed down through the Indians who have lived around San Xavier ever since the days of the jesuits. And, while Mr. Prent Duell, in discussing this tradition, speaks disparagingly of the veracity of the natives, yet his contention that the jesuits laid the foundations of this church is based solely upon an indian tradition to that effect.– C.H.

In a fertile oasis, under clear blue skies, stood the mission San Xavier, nearing completion. For fourteen years brown hands, unskilled in the art of rearing immense structures of brick and stone, had pushed and pulled, lifted and carried, until, step by step, a beautiful church had taken form and risen before the eyes of the people – a miracle to them and to all who since have marveled at its strength, beauty, and majesty.

Even the indian women had contributed their share. These, desiring to serve the woman Mary, mother of Christ, had carried the boulders of which the seven-foot foundation was built from the mountains several miles away; and so devoted were these vigorous Papago women that if by chance one of them let a stone fall, she considered it polluted and, letting it lie where it fell, went back for another.

Brick by brick the solid masonry had arisen. The main dome, masterpiece of architecture, was finished. The unknown artist who had carved the classic façade had laid aside his chisels. Now, Indians of both sexes were furbishing up the interior with its ornate paintings depicting the life of Christ and its exquisite statues carved in the likeness of the sculptor's two daughters – another talented artist whose name is lost to us.

A number of natives worked on the church roof about the unfinished tower. One of the white workmen – a Spaniard named Ganoa – directed the laying of the bricks at the top of the tower, and from time to time called instructions to the Indians on the roof below. From his place on the tower's rim, he could look down through the unfinished interior 90 feet to the stone floor below.

Near the church a group of Indians toiled at making bricks, under the direction of Padre Narisco Guiterrez and the elder Ganoa. In the fields near by other Indians, bare-legged, directed the irrigating waters over the crops with hoes.

Padre Narisco and Ganoa presently were called to the church, and when after a time Ganoa returned to find the workmen taking their ease, he began to harangue them angrily:

"Get busy, you good-for-nothing laggards! Would you be another fourteen years in the building of this church? You are industrious only in resting! Juan, look to the kiln! Basilio, carry these bricks to the dry-ing-ground!"

At a light touch on his arm Ganoa turned impatiently, and came face to face with Padre Baltaser Carillo. The padre rebuked him:

"Have a little patience, my son. You surely have worked with the neophytes long enough to know that they are children, and that we must make allowances for that." Then, turning to one of the workmen,

"I will carry the bricks for you, Basilio, if you are too weary."

"No! No, Padre!" cried the Indian, lifting the board on which the bricks were stacked and hurrying away with them.

Ganoa, gazing up at the walls of the church, remarked:

"If I have been driving our Indians too hard, Padre, it is that your cherished dream may be the sooner realized. Very soon, now, you will see your plans of fourteen years fulfilled."

Padre Baltaser smiled, and then his notice was drawn to one Indian who sulked and muttered words to the other workmen, and gave little attention to his work.

"What is the matter with Ricardo?" the padre asked, in low tones.

"He mopes because I told him he is the laziest Indian in the colony," replied Ganoa. "He can work, but he sulks when I correct him. His example affects the others, too."

Padre Baltaser saw Ricardo's four-year old son, Ricardito, playing near by, and as the boy passed near him, he caught him, pulled his ears, held him up by the heels, tossed him into the air and caught him, while the child shrieked with glee and finally flung his arms about the priest's neck. The padre, glancing sidelong at Ricardo, saw that the ill-humor had disappeared from his face.

The boy settled in the padre's arms and begged, with eyes shining, "Tell story of great dome, Padre!"

Padre Baltaser laughed and, seating himself on a bench, talked to Ricardito in a voice that all could hear:

"Once, Ricardito, when you were no bigger than the cabbages in our fields, a priest living in the San Xavier mission ——"

"You, Padre!" interrupted the child, eagerly.

"There was a priest who wished that his church might have a great and beautiful dome, all lined with gold and pictures, so that it would be a delight to the hearts of his people. Now domes are easy to make, are they not, Ricardito?"

"No! No!"

"Why not?"

"They hi-i-igh, and wi-i-ide!" exclaimed the boy, imitating the priest's voice, and proving that he had heard the story before.

"That is just right, my son. And to make the dome, the workmen used long ladders ——"

"No! No, Padre ——"

"What did they use, Ricardito?"

"They fill church up with earth!"

"What!" cried the priest, in mock dismay, while the brick-makers chuckled with amusement. "But why should they fill their beautiful church with earth?"

"They make earth round on top, like dome, Padre, and make dome over it!"

"Oh——! But the church has no earth in it, Ricardito."

"No!" The child clapped his hands, for now had come the most delightful part of the story, and he carried it on: "The padres hide coins in earth. When people hear, they come – hunt for money and carry away earth – carry away all earth because most coins on floor!"

"So they did, Ricardito, so they did – and the story says that a man named Ricardo carried away the most earth and found the most coins."

The face of the boy's father now glowed with pleasure, and he was working willingly and carefully, stimulating his fellow-laborers by his example.

"You know how to make them work, Padre," said Ganoa, aside. "I wish you would tell me your secret."

"Just patience, my son – and the knowledge that human nature is very much the same the world over."

A native youth now approached Padre Baltaser.

"We start on the dome of tower now, Padre. The

THE SAN XAVIER AS IT APPEARS TODAY

señor on tower he say it is your wish to lay first bricks of dome. He say I tell you, all is ready."

"Thank you, my son. I will come at once."

All in the settlement knew of Padre Baltaser's affection for his new church. He had been its architect; he had secured the funds for its construction. Everyone understood that the beginning of this last dome represented to him the final act of the momentous task that he had undertaken fourteen years before.

The priest stopped before the main entrance and regarded for a time the imposing beauty of the façade. Then he mounted the ladder that leaned against the front wall, to the high window balcony, where he stopped again to view the front with its beautiful statues of Carlos III, Saint Cecelia, Saint Francis, and the Holy Mother in their niches. Then he moved on upward until he stepped over the moorish cornices onto the roof.

Here ladders had been lashed together and propped against the tower. Work inside and outside of that part of the building had ceased, and all waited as the padre stepped upon the ladder. Up and up he climbed, until he reached the very top of the tower, where a supply of brick and mortar had been placed ready for him. Then, seizing a trowel, he leaned far over to lay the first of the dome bricks in place.

Ganoa's cry of warning came too late. There was a sudden loosening of bricks, their mortar yet unset — Padre Baltaser lost his balance, swayed an instant, then plunged headlong into the well of the tower. Ganoa clapped his hands to his eyes; from the workmen came a high-pitched yell of consternation.

By the horrified people below, the padre's gowned

body was glimpsed as it flashed by the tower windows: then there came a rattling of falling bricks on the stone-flagged floor, followed by a muffled crash. All rushed frantically to the base of the tower.

The next day Padre Narisco, who had spent the night watching beside the stilled form of his friend and brother, composedly said the requiem mass over the remains of Padre Baltaser, and the body was laid to rest beneath the flagstone floor where the man had fallen to his death.

Then Padre Narisco conducted the congregation out of the church, where all stood with bared heads before the unfinished tower that now was the headstone of its creator.

"We will go on, my children," spoke Padre Narisco, "as your Padre Baltaser would have us do, and carry out his plans for this mission. But we shall leave this tower as it now is, as a memorial to your padre, that all who see it may be reminded of the sacrifice of the man who died — as most of us die, my children — just before the realization of his dream."

Dorotea's Roses

Six-year old Dorotea Moraga could not understand the long, involved discussion that her father, an officer of the Tubac presidio, was having with his captain, Juan de Anza, as they sat under the huge lamp of the veranda, except that it was about four indian chiefs who lived in a village just over those black mountains behind which the sun set every evening.

Dorotea knew that there were good and bad Indians. Good ones raised crops and went to mass, while bad ones stole cattle and carried off little children when these did not obey their parents. Or so she had been advised by her parents and by her friend, Captain Anza, and she was ready to back the wisdom of these three against the rest of the world.

But the words that her father was using – "rebellion," "hostages," "drastic measures," etc. – sent puckers of bewilderment over her oval face. Then it seemed strange, too, that her father, who always could answer her questions, could not answer the questions that Captain Anza was asking him about the goodness or badness of those four indian chiefs.

So she gave it up, straightened her prim little apron over her plain muslin dress, and proudly plucked at the big bow of pink ribbon tied to her hair. This done, she settled back against her father's broad shoulder and began counting the wrinkles in Captain Anza's

forehead. The little rose-people in the great garden
behind the presidio church, she knew, would want to
be told just how many lines were in the captain's forehead, for they loved her secrets — they had told her
so. She was very glad the rose-people did not use such
large words. They nodded greetings to her when she
skipped among them and they in turn whispered secrets
which she never told a soul. They were her little friends
and she loved to play among them.

After Captain Anza had left her home, Dorotea's
mother came out on the veranda and seated herself
by Moraga, looking at him as she did when about to
ask a question.

"The captain has decided to hold the four sons of
those chiefs as hostages, until the fathers surrender
themselves for trial," Moraga informed his wife. "The
chiefs somehow learned that they were to be arrested,
and they escaped to the mountains. The posse brought
back their four sons.

"We don't know," he went on, "that those chiefs are
guilty of having tried to foment a rebellion, but their
flight strengthens the suspicion that they are culpable.
Anyhow, their sons will be kept in confinement, on
an extremely scanty allowance of food, until the fathers
come in and surrender."

Dorotea heard but failed to comprehend this conversation, and what followed she heard not at all, for
after a while she woke with a start that nearly tumbled
her off her father's lap. Then she felt her mother's
arms lift her, and she heard her mother's soft voice
saying, "This little woman should have been in bed
an hour ago."

"But you know what a favorite she is with the captain," protested the father, gently. "She kept awake as long as he was here."

And the last that Dorotea remembered was that the captain's forehead had three long wrinkles and five short ones. She must tell the rose-people about them. Maybe they could tell her what had brought those wrinkles to her friend's forehead.

The next day, Dorotea hurried from the main presidio building into the garden that nestled against the south and east sides of the church and that ran right up against the east end of the presidio building. She searched through the rosebushes, laughed greetings to the new buds that were unfolding, felt vaguely troubled and grieved over the blossoms that were fading and falling. She scolded tiny, awkward bugs hiding among the flowers, and caught showers of falling petals in her apron. But none of her flower-friends could tell her what made the wrinkles in the captain's forehead.

She followed a path to the northwest corner of the garden, believing that the flowers were expecting her and would be disappointed if she did not visit them all.

Then she heard a strange cry that made her jump behind a rosebush and peer through its foliage toward the barracks, from which the cry seemed to come. Now it came again – she caught the word "hungry!" called distressfully, in a childish voice.

A large red rose was brushing Dorotea's cheek caressingly. "Must I see who it is?" she asked the red rose.

The rose nodded affirmatively.

The child slipped from the garden toward the tower of the barracks, her eyes and ears alert. Then she saw, staring through the small, barred aperture of the prison room at the base of the tower, the brown, distressed face of an indian boy. Now other boyish faces appeared at the opening – four in all, one of them belonging to a boy so small that apparently he had to tiptoe to look over the window-ledge. All began clamoring piteously for food.

A few times, during her play, Dorotea had come close to the tower and had been frightened home by some ugly or vicious face glowering in her direction from the prison window. But these prisoners were children little older than herself, and they were begging, in such Spanish as the padre at the Tumacacori mission had taught them, for food. Dorotea could not understand children being bad enough to be shut up in the prison room of the barracks. It was for bad, very bad, indian men, and for soldiers who got drunk.

So she went up to the window and, while a breeze fanned her hair across her wondering eyes, she studied, dubiously, the pitiful boyish faces before her. Then she asked,

"Are you bad Indians?"

"No! no! We not bad! We good! We hungry! Your chief Anza, he bad, much bad! We good!"

"Captain Anza is not a bad man!" retorted Dorotea.

"But we not bad, too!" insisted the famished boys. "We do nothing! We hungry! We much hungry!"

But Dorotea was incensed at the imputation cast upon the captain, and presently she departed.

However, she was disquieted. These boys, she felt, were not big enough to be bad. But, on the other hand, Captain Anza could do no wrong.

She sought out her father.

"Father," she asked, "what have those four indian boys done that was bad?"

"Why, *chiquita!* Where have you been nosing around?"

She told him how she had discovered the youthful prisoners.

"You shouldn't go there, *cara mía,*" he advised her. "Suppose —" he rolled his eyes in mock alarm— "suppose those indian boys had seized your arm and eaten it off?"

Dorotea shuddered.

"But they haven't been bad, Dorotea. Their fathers have done wrong, and we have put the boys in prison because their fathers have run away instead of coming and confessing that they have done wrong. Do you understand?"

Dorotea partly understood. That is, she understood perfectly that it was cowardly to run from merited punishment. But she couldn't get it quite clear why the boys were being punished.

She returned to the garden and consulted her rose-people. She wanted to feed those boys. The roses swayed to and fro as though nodding agreement with what was in her mind. Her face brightened. She was glad her flower-friends agreed with her.

So she made her way to the presidio kitchen. She knew that the cook – a jovial round man with whiskers like the stuffing in her mother's sofa – was over at the barracks playing cards with the sergeants.

She selected such meat, bread, and fruit as she liked herself, placed it all in her apron, and went unobserved through the garden, around the church and to the prison room. There she thrust the food cautiously, at arm's length, through the bars of the window, where it was eagerly seized by the voracious boys. But none of them attempted to seize her hand and eat it, so she became more confident. She saved one luscious peach for the youngest of the four, who was about her own age, and this she dropped to him while the others were greedily devouring their portions. They didn't thank her, but she knew that an Indian expresses gratitude only by deeds.

Then she slipped back through the garden, where her rose-friends complacently nodded approval of what she had done.

Dorotea repeated this stealthy performance each day for several days. When once out of the big presidio building she was comparatively safe, for the shrubbery of the garden concealed her from observation until she was near the prison room. And before making the final dash across the open between the garden and the barracks, she would pause to survey the situation.

But there were times, when the rose-people were quiet, that the little girl wondered whether or not they were pleased.

Then came an afternoon when the sun's heat made the rose-people droop their heads unhappily, and they did not nod a greeting to her. She felt uneasy as she made her way among them with her apronful of food. It seemed to her that these flower-friends were holding aloof from her.

Her premonitions were realized when, as she was handing the food through the bars to the boys, her father appeared around the corner of the barracks.

Dorotea never had seen her father so angry with her before. He led her back to their quarters in the presidio, and by the time they got there his wrath was somewhat cooled. But he told Dorotea that the indian boys had been imprisoned by order of Captain Anza, and that her act in supplying them with additional food was treason. He concluded his admonitions by warning her that if she did it again his honor as a soldier would compel him to have her arrested and tried as a traitor.

Of course he did not mean this, but Dorotea believed him, and she had been taught to believe that treason is the foulest of all crimes. She had heard of a soldier having been hanged for treason only a few months before, and how he had been buried outside of holy ground.

But she wished that she could understand clearly what was right and what was wrong. Captain Anza could do no wrong. Yet she recalled that when her mother once imprisoned her in her room, as punishment for having pursued her pet chipmunk across the parade-ground while a cavalry-drill was going on, Captain Anza had surreptitiously smuggled a big piece of sweet chocolate to her through her window, and nobody had accused him of treason. Her parents, she knew, did their best to help her understand what was right and what was wrong, but sometimes they left her badly bewildered.

She gave it up, and decided that she would have to consult her flower-friends whenever she wanted to know what was right to do.

The next day it rained, and Dorotea had to remain indoors; but she was glad because she knew that the rose-people would be refreshed by their long, cooling drink of water.

But the following day it was dry enough to play in the garden again, and her ceaseless activities soon took her around the corner of the church. The imprisoned boys caught sight of her through their loophole, and at once set up a clamor for food.

The scene of two days before rose to Dorotea's mind, and she started to retreat. Then she hesitated; she thought she should explain the situation to the indian lads.

So she went up to the window and as soon as she could induce the boys to still their begging, she informed them with great dignity that to bring them anything more to eat would be an act of treason of which she, the daughter of an officer of the king, would not be guilty. But they continued to clamor piteously for food, even after she had patiently explained to them that treason was the blackest of all crimes. They were extremely hungry.

After she had left them, Dorotea's conscience threatened to assail her from both sides. The pleas of the famished boys still rang in her ears – but, treason!

Her flower-friends were drowsing in the warm sunshine, too sleepy to answer her questions.

She finally went into her tiny room in the presidio and spent a very uncomfortable half hour wrestling with her two-faced conscience and debating between duty and inclination.

The upshot of her self-communion was that she stole into the presidio kitchen, filled her apron with an assortment of food, and slipped out into the garden. The rose-people now nodded approval, but this did not entirely remove the misgivings from the little girl's mind.

She had made her way nearly to the rear of the chapel, and was feeling relieved on having about ac-

complished her errand of mercy in safety, when she
saw her father approaching around the church. The
awful enormity of her crime that instant revealed itself to her, and she stopped, suddenly numbed with
terror. Treason! and she the daughter of an officer of
the king!

Her father came up to her and asked, quietly,

"What is it that you have in your apron, Dorotea?"

Her tongue clung to the roof of her mouth and her
blanched lips, parted with fear, moved convulsively.
She could only stare up at her father's face, her eyes
dilated from terror.

"You are a soldier's daughter, Dorotea," she heard
him saying, "and never have lied to me. Tell me what
you have in your apron."

Distractedly the little girl looked about her, in a
desperate appeal to her flower-friends for help! Would
they fail her now when her world was falling? They
seemed to lean eagerly to her, and she gasped despair-
ingly,

"Oh, roses!"

"Bueno," answered her father, "you never yet have
lied to me, and so I will take your word for it." He
started to walk on.

But now Dorotea was stricken anew with horror at
having lied, and worse, she had lied to her father who
trusted her. Better any punishment – better even death –
than the weight of this infamy upon her conscience.
She wanted to call him back. As she looked up, her
rose-friends again were nodding, "Yes! Yes!" So she
cried wildly.

"Fa— father! father!"

The man stopped and turned about inquiringly.

"See – see, father!" gasped the girl, letting go the corners of her apron, and then, overcome, she collapsed to the ground in a fit of uncontrollable weeping.

But it was a mass of beautiful white roses that tumbled from her apron!

The father stood in speechless amazement for a few moments. Then he gathered the hysterically sobbing youngster up in his arms.

When he reported the inexplicable circumstance to Anza, the latter regarded the miraculous transformation of food into roses as a sign indicating the innocence of the four suspected indian chiefs, and he at once ordered that the boys be freed, fed, and sent back with presents to their village.

Dorotea was sorely puzzled. She had expected death as the only punishment that would fit her crime and instead she was greatly petted; even surly Mateo, who rode the big black horse, swept off his hat to her. All this was beyond her understanding.

But her mother answered her questions with, "You will understand when you are older, Dorotea." And her flower-friends, who had not failed her in her crisis, nodded to her, "Wait. One day you will understand."

All this happened more than a century and one-half ago, and the famous Tubac presidio is desolate now. The church is in ruins, and the hand of time has been laid scourgingly upon the other buildings. Behind the stark remains of the fallen church are only traces of the beautiful rose garden where little Dorotea played and talked with her flower-friends.

The matter-of-fact person would, of course, point

out the obvious – that Dorotea had only been gathering roses and that she had been frightened out of her wits by the threatening aspect of her father. But surely it can do no harm to pretend that things happened just as the legend states, and as her father probably believed, they happened. A belief in miraculous happenings still was prevalent in those old days.

SEQUEL

The histories of our southwest speak of one Chief Palma of the Yuma Indians who was the firm friend of Anza and of Anza's people throughout his life.

Those Indians, being unable to conceive of any social structure as vast as a modern nation, assumed that the social and political organization of the Spaniards was similar to their own, where every village, or group of villages, was a distinct people. To them every Spanish colony represented a tribe, or at least a clan, of white men.

So they remained at peace with Anza's people, the while they were intermittently hostile toward the other white people of Sonora.

In 1775 Anza led a swarm of colonists from Mexico through southwestern Arizona to California, crossing the Colorado river near the present town of Yuma. While these colonists were not from Anza's district, he was their leader, and the Yuma Indians logically assumed that they were of the white tribe ruled by Anza. Consequently, not only did these Indians allow the colonists unhindered passage through their territory, but aided them materially in crossing the Colorado river.

Five years later the two settlements known as the

Colorado river missions were established on the lower Colorado river, just below the junction of the Gila. The colonists sent to these two outposts utterly disregarded the rights of the Yuma Indians, and the Indians, tried to the limit of endurance, planned the utter destruction of the two settlements.

Just as the blow was about to fall upon the doomed but unsuspecting Spaniards, another expedition of colonists similar to the one led by Anza six years earlier arrived over the same route, bound for California. Chief Palma, believing these to be more of Anza's people, held his tribe in leash until they were gone.

So for some days, while the California-bound colonists tarried at the Colorado river settlements, the impending catastrophe was held in check. Then, as soon as they were out of the way, the blow fell and not one Spaniard of the river settlements was spared. After the massacre all the buildings were destroyed.

Now the native story-tellers assure us that Chief Palma was the father of the youngest of the four boys whom Dorotea had fed some ten years before.

If so, we naturally wonder whether any of those California-bound colonists ever learned that they had passed safely through the shadow of death only because of the Indians' love for the stalwart Anza and his little friend Dorotea; and whether Dorotea, who at the time was living in California, ever knew that these colonists owed their lives to her because of the indian boys she had surreptitiously fed.

Treasure Legends of Arizona

While the treasure legends of New Mexico and Texas have their roots in the *gran quivira* myth, which has been discussed in the group of general legends, those of Arizona spring from traditions of gold and silver mined under the supervision of the padres of two of the missions, the San José de Tumacacori and the San Bernardino.

In neither case is there any foundation in authentic history for these stories. There is practically conclusive evidence that no mining of any kind was carried on by the franciscan missions, and outside of southern Arizona no other order carried on any missionary work in our southwestern states. The franciscan padres had observed the results to the indian population of the opening of mines in other districts and they wanted none of it. There is a California legend to the effect that the padres of one mission deliberately suppressed the news of the discovery of gold within their territory.[45]

There is a possibility that the jesuits, who were in charge of the missions of Arizona and Sonora up to 1768, may have carried on placer mining, but this never has been proved. However, the indian traditions to the effect that mines were worked by certain missions are too numerous and too much in agreement to be entirely ignored.

---

[45] Sanchez, *Spanish and indian place names of California,* 220.

THE LOST MINE OF THE TUMACACORI

Forty-five miles south of Tucson in the Santa Cruz
valley, and about four miles from Tubac, lie the ruins
of the once pretentious mission of San José de Tumacacori. One time a center of industry, it is a scene of
utter desolation now; its old gardens and orchards are
quite obliterated and given over to the sparse, tough
growths of the desert, and gray lizards bask in the
sunshine on crumbling walls laid by hands that themselves have long since crumbled into dust.

The country around the Tumacacori – but not in the
vicinity of that mission – has been a mining region
from the earliest pioneer days. In the Spanish period
some mines were operated in a primitive fashion in
the mountains walling the Santa Cruz valley. Some of
the richest gold and silver mines ever found on this
continent were just across the border of Arizona in
Mexico. In one locality less than 50 miles from the
Tumacacori a great deposit of silver nuggets was found
in 1736 just below the surface of the ground, some of
the nuggets weighing a ton or more each. The largest
one weighed between 3,500 and 4,000 pounds. This is
not a tradition, but an historical fact.

When the United States purchased from Mexico the
territory known as the Gadsden purchase, south of the
Gila river, it was primarily in order to secure what
was believed to be rich mining territory. The first
Anglo-americans to come into that region (Poston and
his company in 1856) came for the purpose of reopen-
ing mines that had been worked by the Spaniards, as
well as to prospect for new ones.

Such is the authentic historical background.

It is a tradition that the priests of the Tumacacori

mission, which lies within the Gadsden purchase, carried on mining as one of their activities, both during
the jesuit regime and the subsequent rule of the franciscans, and it is known that the collapse of the buildings was not brought about by wind and storm, but by
the excavations of Mexican and Anglo-american treas-
ure-seekers, for the Anglo adventurer was no whit
behind his Latin neighbor in his desire for unearthed
wealth.

The tower of the Tumacacori church contained two
tiny apertures, or peepholes, one in the west and the
other in the east wall, and it is said that one looking
eastward through these holes would be looking directly
on the spot, far away near the horizon, where the mined
gold and silver were stored. It also is asserted that
markers or guide posts were set up at intervals along
the route to this wealth and one person of the writer's
acquaintance claimed to have seen in the mountains
east of the Tumacacori an enormous boulder on which
was engraved an arrow pointing eastward, and above
the arrow the scallop-shell symbol of the order of friars
minor.

However, the tower of the Tumacacori has been in
ruins for three-quarters of a century, and any guide
monuments that may have been erected have disappeared, so that the story cannot be verified.

There is one story to the effect that the wealth was
secreted in a cave, to which was fitted a heavy oaken
door set flush with the rock wall of the canyon in which
the cave was located, and that the door was weathered
to the same color as the rock, so that an unobservant
person might pass it without seeing it. It is said that
once a man, lost in the labyrinthine hills somewhere

east of the Tumacacori mission, encountered this door but, knowing nothing of the legend associated with it, he supposed it to be the entrance to some prospector's abandoned quarters. He later was unable to relocate it.

While the present writers discredit this story, this man's inability to find the door afterward is entirely plausible. The writers themselves, in similar country, have been within 50 yards of a known spot they were seeking, without finding it or realizing its proximity.

This legendary sequel to the mine of the Tumacacori has bred innumerable stories of attempts – most of them nearly successful –to find the secreted wealth, and the story of this golden cache itself is told with many minor variations. One version has it that the door is the entrance to the mine rather than to the stored bullion; another version states that the door is not of oak, but of iron. The story has been used as the plot for a well-known novel.

Search for this wealth still is made; there is now on foot (1937) a scheme to conduct a systematic search for the mysterious door. If found, it doubtless will prove to be what its first finder supposed it to be – the abandoned quarters of some early prospector.

THE TAIOPA MINE

The Taiopa mine was located, supposedly, somewhere in southeastern Arizona or northwestern Sonora. It is said to have been unbelievably rich and was in territory possessed by the Pima Indians. It is claimed that this mine was near the mission of San Bernardino, which lies just across the Arizona boundary in Sonora, and that it was worked under the supervision of the padres of that mission.

The tradition persists among the Pima Indians today that the Taiopa mine was worked under the supervision of the jesuits of San Bernardino and that, when in 1767 came the royal order for all jesuits to leave Spanish territory, the padres of this mission told the Indians that some day they would return and, while it might be many years, the Indians were to keep a fire always burning at the mine, to guide the returning padres to it.

The jesuit fathers never came back. But the Indians, generation after generation, faithfully kept the fire burning and with the passage of time it became a tradition that some day those same "black robes" would return. And so the fire never has been allowed to die. Somewhere, say the Pimas, in the bewildering maze of the mountain fastnesses of that region the fire burns still.

No record of any such mine has yet been found in the archives of Mexico. If there was such a mine, and it was worked by the jesuits, it is not probable that any record of it ever will be found in secular archives. But some of the Pima Indians today claim to know its approximate location. It is a fact that for many years after the first Anglo-americans came into south-eastern Arizona the Pimas frequently sold them quantities of ore that was very rich, but these natives could be neither persuaded nor coerced into revealing the source of this ore. They declared that the curse of the "black robes" would fall upon whoever revealed the location of the mine.

None of this ore has been brought in for many years, and it is conjectured that the Indians who knew the exact location of the mine are now all dead and that their confinement upon a reservation has prevented their showing the mine to any of their children. This supposition, however, does not harmonize very well with the tradition that the fire still is kept burning.

The story still is current through southern Arizona of how a Mexican woman once was permitted to visit the Taiopa mine.

She had taken care of a Pima chief through a long illness, and upon his recovery he gave her some pieces of ore containing a high percentage of free gold. This roused a good deal of excitement in her village, and she was urged to prevail upon the chief to show her the source of the ore. At length he yielded to her importunities and consented.

But she was disappointed in her hopes. She was conducted by two indian women who adopted the precaution of traveling only at night and in addition blindfolding the Mexican woman while traveling. On the morning after the fourth night the mine was reached, and the woman was permitted to gather up some of the ore to take back to her village as proof that she had visited the mine. That evening she again was blindfolded and conducted from the scene. Only two nights' travel was required to reach home; she, therefore, was evidently led back over a different route and a much shorter one.

The woman retained no idea of the direction in which she had traveled, and the distance could have been anything up to two nights' travel.

There are several traditions as to what the padres of the San Bernardino did with the bullion obtained from the Taiopa mine, but the most persistent is that they buried it somewhere on the mission grounds. The Mexicans of southeastern Arizona tell many tales of the attempts to find this wealth, and it appears that the grounds of the San Bernardino, like those of the Tumacacori, have been pretty well burrowed.

The Treasure of the San Bernardino

More than a century ago there lived in the town of Arispe in Sonora two young Mexicans, Felix and Tomas, both of whom were paying their addresses to a young belle named Liseta.

Liseta showed no partiality toward either of her suitors, and between the two it was hard indeed to choose, even had the señorita been so inclined. They were equally poor, and neither had any well-defined project for legitimately increasing his holdings of worldly goods, or for what the unromantic practical world calls "earning a living." Both could play the guitar well, they smoked about the same number of brown *cigarros* daily, and any insurance company would have accepted either of them as a gilt-edge risk against dying of overwork.

Although rivals, there was no animosity between them. Liseta's father was prosperous and had many men in his employ. It was agreed between the twain that whichever finally won the provoking Liseta was to see that the loser was provided with a good position with Liseta's father – a position carrying ample remuneration with a minimum of work.

One day a newcomer, Rafael Perez by name, appeared and in the course of events made the acquaintance of Felix, Tomas, and Liseta. He made no attempt, apparently, to enter the lists himself, but contented himself with an occasional dance or horseback ride with the señorita. So Tomas and Felix, who at first had been somewhat disturbed over Rafael's acquaintance with Liseta, regained their equanimity and looked upon Rafael with tolerance.

Now these two spent much of their time seeking hidden treasure – in their imaginations – and often had discussed the hidden wealth of the San Bernardino. They told Rafael of it, and how they would have sought and obtained it did the enterprise not involve so much physical exertion.

Two days later Rafael disappeared and was gone three weeks. When he returned, he called Felix and Tomas into conference.

"Over a year ago," he informed them, "I came into possession of an old parchment. I thought it a hoax at the time but when you gentlemen told me of the buried treasure of the Taiopa mine, I began to wonder. So I decided to investigate.

"Now, before I go on, I ask you this: If I should put you in the way of recovering that wealth, would you agree to turn over to me one third of it? I will give you my reason, presently, for not going with you."

Tomas and Felix agreed eagerly to this proposition.

"Gentlemen," Rafael resumed, "I am a fugitive from justice. I am wanted up in Tucson. The officers of the border know my face. That is the reason I dare not go up there."

He now drew a discolored piece of parchment from his pocket and unfolded it on the table, while his two auditors bent eagerly over it.

"Here," said Rafael, pointing, "is the old San Bernardino church. Here is the convento. This double line is the old road past the mission. Now you see this little cross just outside the altar end of the church?"

Their eyes had followed his finger over the diagram. He now turned the parchment over and announced, "Now what do you make of that?"

There, near the top of the dingy sheet, were the letters: DLSSPE EAVCEN BCAISP ARREOA JUANSR OZSMOR DDDIRA EOOLOS. Below these was the symbol of the order of Jesus.

"A cipher," exclaimed Rafael, to his puzzled associates. "I solved it. If you select the first letter from each of these groups, then the second, and so on, you get the words *'Debajo de la cruz, dos varas. Dos cien mil pesos oro en barras.'*" (Two *varas* under the cross. Two hundred thousand dollars in gold bullion.)

"Gentlemen, when I left here three weeks ago, I went to the border and located the ruins of the San Bernardino. And there, on the east end of the church, I found a small cross cut into the wall.

"What did I do? I came back as far as Agua Prieta, intending there to secure some pack-mules and tools for digging. But there I ran into a police officer who recognized me, and I was almost caught. I dare not go back; they are watching for me.

"Now, gentlemen, this parchment shows you the exact point at which to dig. I shall trust to your honor to make a fair division with me when you return."

Felix and Tomas left the conference in a state of bewildered excitement. It seemed incredible that so much wealth should be within their reach.

The next morning they sold their meager possessions, even parting from their beloved guitars, and invested the proceeds in food, a number of strong bags, a lantern, a pick, and a shovel. They had no money left with which to hire pack-mules, but an obliging neighbor, being informed they were going after a load of valuable freight, lent them six mules on credit to be paid for upon their return. Then they set out, carrying provisions for 25 days, although they calculated the entire trip would not consume more than seventeen days.

When they arrived at the old mission, they found that everything was as Rafael had said. They drove their mules into a ruined part of the church, and there concealed themselves, for there was a hacienda less than half a mile north of the ruins.

As they impatiently awaited darkness, they discussed in low, excited tones what they would do with their wealth. One hundred thousand dollars apiece! For they had no intention of sharing with Rafael. If he protested, they would turn him over to the authorities for transportation to Tucson to answer for his crime, whatever it was.

With nightfall, they lighted their lantern and began to dig, one loosening the earth with the pick, then resting while the other shoveled it away. The digging was easier than they had expected to find it, and after the first foot or two there was no need for the pick.

After two hours Tomas, who was shoveling, struck something that gave forth a metallic sound. A few more hurried shovelfuls, and the implement scraped on metal again. Felix, no longer able to restrain himself, flung himself down with a yell and began clawing into the loose earth with his hands. Tomas, equally excited, dropped the shovel and followed suit. In their frenzied clawing, they interfered with each other, and unreasoning anger began to mix with their other emotions. Then, as Felix forcibly hurled Tomas out of the way, Tomas seized the shovel and smote Felix broadside on the side of the head with it, knocking him senseless.

Tomas then dropped to his knees in the middle of the pit, clawing and digging, until he seized and drew forth – an old iron bucket! A bucket, battered and worn, but unrusted.

For a few moments he sat panting, bewildered. Then, with an outburst of cursing, he flung the bucket out of the pit and clambered out himself.

A moment later Felix came to and sat up, his head in a whirl. To his ears came the sound of lamenting and profanity. Still somewhat dizzy from the blow he had received, he set the lantern out of the pit and then managed to climb out himself. There he saw Tomas, in a towering rage, piling their supplies upon one of the mules, and kicking the unoffending brute savagely while so doing.

The idea suddenly was born in Felix's mind that Tomas had secured the treasure and was making off with it. Screaming "Thief! Miscreant!" he flung himself at Tomas, and that gentleman, aching for some one upon whom to spend his rage, met the attack willingly.

For several minutes the two rolled and tumbled in the dust, pommeling and choking each other. Finally Tomas rose, victor, and spat out a mouthful of sand and gravel. He had a rapidly-swelling eye, but Felix had lost three of his front teeth.

Now Tomas seized the old bucket and thrust it before Felix's face.

"Look at that!" he snarled. "There was nothing else in that cursed pit!"

Felix looked. One look was sufficient, and he hurled

the bucket with a resounding bang against the wall of the church and broke into wild lamentations.

Then Tomas yelled, angrily,

"Get up, fool, and help pack the mules! What are you ——" Tomas stopped abruptly, then sank, overcome, to the ground. The mules were gone! Through the still night air came the eager galloping of homeward-bound hoofs.

Tomas sat, with his head between his hands, saying nothing. Felix also sat down, sobbing audibly. They felt undone – utterly undone. One of the mules had even carried away their store of provisions.

They did not start back until morning. The supplies carried by the laden mule were found scattered along the trail for three miles, and the two young men gathered up what they could carry. Each day, as they made their footsore way toward Arispe, they salved their bitter disillusionment with exclamatory talk of what they would do to Rafael Perez. Ah, but they held a sword over his head that he had not thought of! He had made a false move in confiding to them that he was a fugitive from justice!

When, after nine days on the trail, they limped wearily into Arispe, they decided to go, just as they were, to Liseta's home.

"When she sees us," declared Tomas, "and learns what we have suffered for her sake, she will be suffocated with compassion. We shall be heroes in her eyes."

"That is so," assented Felix. "A woman loves the man who adventures all things for her. It is well that Liseta shall see upon us the evidence of the trials we have undergone as knights of hers."

Arriving at Liseta's home, they were met at the door

by a servant who eyed them with suppressed amusement.

"Oh," said the servant, in reply to their inquiry, "the
Señorita Liseta? But she is now the Señora Perez. Yes!
She married the Señor Rafael Perez six days gone, and
departed with him to his father's hacienda – the hacienda on which the old mission of San Bernardino is
situated, Señors!"

There may be some truth in the foregoing story for
we find that in 1822 a ranch of nearly 75,000 acres, on
which are the ruins of the San Bernardino mission, was
granted by the Mexican government to one Ignacio
Perez, and that it remained in the possession of his
descendants until 1884.

California Legends

California Legends

California, although the last of Spain's frontier provinces to be occupied, possesses many interesting legends of the Spanish days. Also, like New Mexico and Texas, California has many little stories of the pioneer period that, while of local interest, treat mostly of simple episodes that could be adequately presented in one or two paragraphs each.

Of those offered our readers all are more or less well known in California, but apparently little known outside that state. Even the most interesting one, which in the past has been related by the historian, the dramatist, and the poet, is not often heard of outside California. It is related according to short-story technique, to which treatment it readily lends itself.

Since the missions were the most important feature of Spanish California, most of the legendary lore centers about these institutions. Four of the seven stories that are reproduced are of this type.

In addition to these, there are several other interesting legends of California that have been preserved by Chase and Saunders.

The Pearl that Defeated Vizcaino

Legend claims for its own many stirring romances created, fostered, or destroyed through a quest for pearls; but legend boasts no love token of greater moment than the pearl that defeated Vizcaino and filled the place of a jewel that never was.

At the time that the Conde de Monterey was viceroy of New Spain, he had in his employ in the viceregal palace of Mexico City a young dandy named Don Lopé, serving in the capacity of a page. Lopé had been reared in luxury and idleness and he shrank from dangers and hardships as one would shrink from contamination.

Nevertheless, he now often wished his body were great and sturdy like that of the burly *cargador* who strode arrogantly past his window each day, and that his face were browned and rugged like that of his patrón, Monterey. For he had fallen in love with the Señorita Elvira, and her attitude toward him was one that no real man would tolerate. She chose to watch him on the one hand, as a mother guards a delicate child, and on the other hand, to ridicule him with eyes that were living, stinging denunciations.

There came an evening when Elvira, in response to his declaration of love and loyalty, frankly expressed to him the thoughts that he already had vaguely guessed.

"I appreciate your devotion, Don Lopé," she told him, "but I haven't a very exalted opinion of your courage and resourcefulness. The man I marry must prove to me his capacity for meeting the world and standing up under its buffetings."

Lopé shifted uneasily in his velvet-and-silk attire, and avoided the steady gaze of the girl. He wondered if she knew she was being cruel. But she went on, inexorably,

"The position of page to the viceroy is hardly a dignified post for a grown man, Don Lopé. In these stirring frontier days, with opportunities waiting on every hand, there is no excuse for any man wasting his years in ease and luxury."

Lopé winced and was silent. He suspected that the girl was leading up to some arduous commission that she wanted him to execute. She waited. Then:

"I love you, Elvira," he declared, raising his eyes to those of the girl. "Name your demands – tell me what I shall do."

Elvira pondered a moment, studying the young man.

"I will set you a task, Don Lopé," she then announced. "You have heard of the exploring and pearl-seeking expedition about to be undertaken by Sebastian Vizcaino?"

Lopé nodded, knowing what was to come.

"I have lost my largest and finest pearl, Don Lopé," she went on. "If you will join Vizcaino's expedition and bring back to me a pearl to match the one I have lost, I will marry you."

Lopé felt suddenly suffocated. She was asking the impossible. He remembered that when, a week before, his patrón had directed him to lift a large box to the table, even that light effort had caused a painful strain in his back that had lasted for several days. How, then, could he survive the arduous labor and the vicissitudes of a long exploring expedition? He had had pointed out to him, only that day, three of the muscular fellows who were to be of Vizcaino's crew. Any one of them could have crushed him.

He looked beseechingly into Elvira's eyes, but they were unyielding.

"I – I cannot go – Elvira," he pleaded. "One day of that life would kill me!"

"Nevertheless, that is my ultimatum," she answered. "You might not find it so unendurable as you imagine, nor would you die so easily as you fear." She rose, indicating that the interview was ended.

The young man stumbled away, resentful, yet realizing that he was not a man, but a coward, weak of body and infirm of purpose.

The following day the Señorita Elvira sought and was granted an audience with the viceroy.

As a result, Lopé was later summoned into the viceroy's presence.

"You are dismissed from service here," announced Monterey, without preliminaries, "and you will report for duty to Sebastian Vizcaino's headquarters at Zacatula. You are to join his expedition, and serve in whatever capacity he may assign to you. One of his officers is awaiting you, and he will attend to the matter of your equipment. Go."

Lopé was dazed. But he knew that the viceroy's will was law. He stumbled out into the anteroom, where he found one of Vizcaino's officers, and the two departed together.

The young man never forgot that first day at sea, nor the days that followed. In comparison to the cramped, dark forecastle of the ship, the quarters in the viceregal palace that had been his home for three years now assumed sybaritic qualities never before dreamed of. His slight frame ached inside his sailor's coarse leathern armor, which fitted him grotesquely. One look at the rough food that was to be his fare filled him with revulsion. As an untrained ordinary seaman, the most objectionable tasks were his, and there were sneers, ridicule, and sometimes physical violence from his fellow sailors. In an indiscreet moment he had revealed to one of them his former mode of living, and as a result he was assailed with all the opprobrious epithets that the imagination of his fellows could devise.

With his misery, Lopé's resentment toward Elvira rose to fury, for he well knew who had prompted the viceroy's drastic action. He felt that he hated her.

Then there was gradually born in him the determination to face the trial through like a man and to return, a man, to fling his contempt in her face. A boyish attitude, truly, but in the end it proved his regeneration.

Except in midsummer, the Gulf of California is stormy and treacherous, and never was it more so than during the months when Vizcaino's three ships were fighting their way toward its head. Every day there was the struggle against gales and contrary head winds. Frequently Lopé dropped from complete exhaustion.

But the indomitable spirit that was developing within him held him to his work. Seven months were consumed in battling the winds up the gulf, and during that time the young Lopé became transformed from a soft, shrinking dandy into a bronzed and muscular seaman. The contempt and abuse from the other sailors had given way to comradeship; and to admiration when, one day early in october, Lopé had cleanly whipped the big, burly coxswain of the ship, in a long-drawn-out fight in which Lopé's agility and endurance triumphed over his opponent's greater size and strength. His face retained its large, questioning black eyes, but it had been browned and hardened by work and by the searching sea air; his armor now clung snugly to a toughened, muscular body, and his former dainty, mincing step had become converted into a firm, swinging stride.

The young man's mental outlook and attitude had undergone a transformation, too. He looked back upon his previous effeminate existence with repugnance and a feeling of shame. In fact, his fight with the coxswain had resulted from that worthy individual's indiscreet reference to Lopé's former mode of life. Lopé's hostility toward Elvira, which had endured during the first two or three months of the voyage, had given way to a feeling of deeper respect and admiration for that clear-sighted young woman.

And through it all he had kept in mind the other object of his voyage – to secure the pearl that Elvira desired – for he had come to feel that the securing of such a pearl would be his insignia of manhood.

But pearls had taken on a fabulous value, now that he came to realize the difficulty of securing them. Indians had told the Spaniards of rich pearl fisheries in the upper Gulf of California; but Indians had been known to direct white men hither and yon for reasons of their own. Lopé had seen no pearls.

When they were about halfway up the gulf, a large number of Indians came down to the shore from their village, and they by gestures invited the white men to land for a visit, showing by pantomime that they had left their weapons at the village a few hundred yards distant. Accordingly, Vizcaino, whose ship was leading, signaled his other two ships that a landing would be made, since it was a part of his commission to win the friendship and goodwill of the natives. Three boats – one from each ship – put off, carrying a total of 45 men. Lopé was in the boat from the flagship, and he was filled with pride for Vizcaino had selected him from the whole crew to command the boat. As a friendly gesture on his part, Vizcaino had ordered his men to leave their weapons on board their ships.

The natives, reassured by the friendly attitude of the white men, flocked to the beach in large numbers, men and women alike, until they outnumbered the Spaniards more than ten to one.

Then followed a cordial exchange of presents, wherein the white men traded beads, bright trinkets, and gaily-colored cloth for fresh drinking water, fish, beans, squash, and dried meats.

Finally, to cement the friendship thus auspiciously formed, pipes were brought, the Indians furnishing the pipes and Vizcaino the tobacco.

Lopé, however, did not smoke. He loitered near the edge of a throng of natives, studying them with interest, and reflecting upon how terrified he had been at the first appearance of untamed Indians six months before. Near by was an indian maiden, whom Lopé observed casually. It was evident from her manner and dress that she was a chief's daughter.

Then, with a sudden movement, this girl turned to speak to her neighbor, and the wind, lifting her hair away from her throat, revealed lying against her brown skin and lodged in a crude shell ornament the most magnificent pearl Lopé ever had beheld!

A moment more and he had sprung forward, knocked aside an intervening native, grasped the ornament from the girl's neck and was darting through the throng toward the boats; all before the startled assemblage could understand what was happening.

Uproar and confusion followed. The Indians were enraged, not because the trinket had been seized – it would have been given to Lopé had he asked it – but because one of their number had been unceremoniously knocked down! The yells of the Indians sent the Spaniards flying toward their boats, not knowing what had happened, but eager to escape before the Indians could get their weapons. It was a frightened and undignified crew that piled into the boats and pulled for deep water.

The Spaniards were pursued by flights of arrows. Many of them were struck, but their heavy leathern armor protected them from injury. Just as the party in Lopé's boat was settling down to a steady rhythm of rowing, an arrow struck one of the men full in the face. Crazed with pain and trying to dislodge the missile, he floundered about, stirring the men into great disorder until, in the tumult, the boat capsized.

Before the other two boats could turn about and come to their assistance, all but five of the men, handicapped by their stiff armor, were drowned. Lopé was one of the five who had strength enough to keep afloat until help arrived.

Vizcaino was so saddened by this disaster that he put his ships about and sailed for home. But Lopé, while grieved by the death of his comrades, also had cause to rejoice for he still had the pearl, concealed in his corselet.

Arrived at Zacatula, Lopé hurried on to Mexico City. There, after he had removed his beard and made himself otherwise as presentable as possible, he called on the Señorita Elvira, feeling sure that the pearl he had for her would surpass in size and beauty the one she had lost.

He had been absent about a year and Elvira failed to recognize him. This muscular, browned face, with its stern mouth and steady, arrogant eyes, was not the face of the Lopé she had known.

But when Lopé convinced her of his identity, he had the keen pleasure of seeing her, in her turn, lower her eyes in confusion.

Then he produced the pearl and laid it in her lap with the careless air of dispensing a glass bead. Elvira started and gasped at the sight of it.

"There is the pearl you sent me for, Señorita," he told her. "But since my going was not of my own volition, I cannot in honor hold you to your part of the contract. The pearl is yours, unconditionally, to replace the one you lost."

Elvira again lowered her eyes, and confessed, meekly:

"But I – I did not lose a pearl, Lopé. I wanted to test your valor – I so wanted you to be a man. I – I will marry you – if you wish – Lopé."

The hostility of the Indians, resulting from Lopé's

act, prevented any settlement being made in Lower California for half a century and, since the occupation of our present state of California could not be undertaken until Lower California was occupied, the settlement of California by the Spanish was delayed a full century.

The legend probably is true, but is not historically verifiable, except that history does record that Vizcaino's expedition was defeated through the rash act of one man in the party who knocked down an unoffending Indian, and that in fleeing to their ships one boatload of men was upset and all but five of them drowned. – C.H.

The Relief of San Diego de Acalá

For the founding of the first Spanish settlement in California, three small ships, laden with supplies, were dispatched from La Paz, while a land expedition commanded by Governor Portolá and accompanied by the great missionary, Junipero Serra (who was ill at the time) made its toilsome way up the peninsula of Lower California to the site selected for the new colony.

One of the ships, the San José, was lost at sea with all on board, and the cargoes of the other two were damaged by sea water before finally reaching San Diego Bay. One of the two that reached this destination was unable to return because of sickness in the crew; the other, the San Antonio, was at once dispatched to Mexico for additional supplies. The sea route to the base of supplies (La Paz) was all of 1000 miles, and the best that could be expected of the San Antonio was that she might make the trip in two months, or anywhere up to six months – or not at all for the waters were stormy and treacherous.

The fact that California now is under the United States flag instead of the British, we owe solely to the tenaciousness of this little colony. The British at that time were claiming the Pacific coast from Alaska to Mexico, and the Hudson's Bay company was planning to plant a colony in California, which the English called New Albion. Hence the occupation of this province by the Spanish in 1769. – C.H.

As the first signs of spring appeared in 1770 at San Diego there were times when Padre Junipero Serra, his mind cleared by returning health and strengthened by deep conviction, lifted his prayers for succor to the very throne of God. In all his life he never had striven so fervently to understand the great will to whose service he had devoted his life.

Before him lay the glorious opportunity of securing Alta California for God and saving the souls of thousands of savages – if only additional supplies for the starving colony about him would arrive in time. Upon a few casks of biscuit seemed to rest the fate of this Pacific paradise!

But the friar, chastening his doubts by long hours of devotion, reasoned that God had walked with him along the way by miraculously healing his affliction, by preserving him from hostile Indians, by saving him from death by scurvy. Clearly God was with him still, and would reveal His purpose in the end.

Then, encouraged by renewed hope, the man would leave the hut dedicated as a temporary church and seek his companions, trying to impart to their waning spirits some of his own steadfastness and faith.

Governor Portolá, disheartened by his unsuccessful search for Monterey Bay, where he had been instructed to plant a second colony, was not to be cheered. He had but one reply to the friar's insistence that they stay in this territory whether or not the San Antonio arrived by the day set for departure: that his company of men must have more than spiritual sustenance. For Portolá had determined that the colony would return to Mexico unless the San Antonio appeared before the twentieth of march.

Padre Serra, saddened by the attitude of those about him, would walk through the rude huts and out of the palisaded inclosure to the crest of the hill at whose base the colony was located. With hand-shaded eyes he would gaze long over the uneasy sea, watching and praying for the San Antonio.

Slowly the days dragged by. Long since, the meager provisions had been divided by Portolá; one part apportioned for their use until the day of departure, the other set aside for the return journey down the long peninsula to La Paz. To the eyes now staring anxiously and fruitlessly over the gray-green waters, the ocean seemed never so infinite, so cruelly barren, so mocking.

With the month of march moving forward, Portolá's men began final preparations for leaving the territory. Padre Serra, however, and his brother missionary, Crespí, while clinging to the belief that the San Antonio yet would arrive in time, nevertheless were firm in their resolve to remain, whatever happened.

Padre Serra was blessed with that divine courage that springs from complete detachment from things mortal. His life he valued not at all, asking only the privilege of yielding it in his Master's service. He could not bring himself to admit defeat in this enterprise in which all the north country lay at stake. He never had admitted defeat, and consequently he never yet had been defeated! The English and Russians were creeping southward on the Pacific coast, and it was not for nothing that King Carlos had ordered his viceroy to "fortify and hold San Diego Bay and Monterey Bay for God and the king of Spain!"

Governor Portolá, always practical, often now pointed out to the indomitable priest that the patron saint of the expedition, San José, and even God Himself, must disapprove of the project that had been undertaken, for had not every conceivable obstacle been placed in their path to turn them back? Was not the very ship that had been christened and dedicated to San José overwhelmed and sent to the bottom of the sea?

The two men, one conscious of spiritual responsibilities and the other aware only of physical needs, could not understand each other. Yet both were natural leaders of men; both were at heart devoted to the work they had been commissioned to do.

Finally, on the tenth day of march – ten days before the time set for departure – a nine days' public prayer was begun to Saint Joseph. All the company joined in the devotions, though some less fervently than others, for some of the men hoped to return to Mexico. Each day, when the meeting disbanded, the friars with hands clasped in constant prayer would climb the hill behind the mission to search the horizon for a sail.

Saint Joseph's day, the nineteenth of march, arrived. Shortly before dawn Padre Serra, having passed a sleepless night, stationed himself on top the hill and waited patiently for sunrise. "The San Antonio will come today," he whispered to himself. "There is yet time."

As morning dawned, many of the company of men joined the friar. Some soon were called back to assist with the final details that attend leave-taking. The priest prayed that something might arise to prevent the going on the morrow. He saw, as clearly as any one, that if this attempt were a failure, no further effort would be made to occupy and hold California during his lifetime and that the richest district of the Pacific would be yielded to the English.

Noon came. "There is yet time," he told himself.

Afternoon came. "There is yet time!"

Evening drew near. "There is yet—" The man flung up his arms in thanksgiving and turned to face his companions. But already they were shouting,

"A SAIL! A SAIL!"

And there far out over the dancing waters a ship lay against the horizon. It was coming nearer.

Now up the hill from the settlement came running the rest of the company. Shouts of joy and thanksgiving rang through the air. Padre Serra stood quietly beside his comrades, filled with the glory of a faith confirmed.

When all had seen the approaching vessel, they knelt while Serra offered up a prayer of gratitude.

But when the men rose to their feet, they saw with amazement and consternation that the ship had disappeared!

Governor Portolá looked at Serra.

"The San Antonio will come," calmly announced the priest. "That was a sign given us, bidding us wait."

So the departure that was to have been made the next morning was postponed another day.

The next afternoon the ship again appeared – and again disappeared! The men grew apprehensive. Portolá hesitated about extending the time for departure a second time. But Serra's faith prevailed.

The same thing happened on the third day, but in answer to Serra's impassioned pleas, Portolá granted one day more, declaring it would be the last.

On the morning of the fourth day, the tension was felt by every one except Serra. Even his brother priest, Padre Crespí, was wavering. Officers and soldiers grouped themselves within the stockade and discussed the mysterious phenomenon with fear and misgiving. What meant the appearing and vanishing of this mystic ship? Might it not be the work of satan, to hold them there for some pending disaster? So argued the men.

Governor Portolá, the man of decision, was bewildered. Only the serene confidence of Junipero Serra was able momentarily to reassure him now. Alone, he began to suspect that their intense desire to see the San Antonio was unseating their reason, or making them subject to hallucinations.

Their fear and restlessness drove the men from the stockade shortly after noon, and the hill became peopled with anxious watchers.

Then, while the missionaries and their companions waited for a repetition of the miracle, a ship came up over the horizon and slowly drifted toward them.

The men watched tensely, breathlessly.

"The phantom ship is earlier than usual!" cried one man, half-jestingly, half-hysterically.

"It does not disappear!" exclaimed another.

"It is the San Antonio!" cried Padre Serra, confidently.

But the men remained skeptical and half-afraid. Thrice they had been deceived and mocked by that apparition.

Closer approached the ship, and now the watchers could discern men in the riggings, trimming and taking in sail as though preparing to anchor. But there came no sound as the ghostly ship drifted in closer and closer.

Then to the ears of the tense watchers on the hill there came the harsh jangle of a heavy chain racing through its locker-port, and a wild yell of exultation rose from their throats. There was nothing unsubstantial about that metallic clangor – the ship had let go her anchor! It was the San Antonio! The colony was saved!

The appearance of a ship over the horizon, four days before the San Antonio arrived, and its reappearance on the two succeeding days, is accepted by several historians, who, however, claim that it was the San Antonio and that for three successive days she was beaten back by contrary head winds. This may be true, but on that coast the stronger head winds are farther south, and a ship that could run them ought then to make the port of San Diego easily. One writer suggests that the mystic ship really was a hallucination, but it is hardly probable that all the men were subject to the same aberration. The present writer suggests a mirage effect; mirages equally remarkable have been cited by the eminent English meteorologist, Sir Napier Shaw.

Chapman asserts that there is no historical foundation for the foregoing legend, although it is conceded that from some cause Portolá delayed departure after having completed preparations to leave San Diego Bay. – C.H.

The Serra Tree

On the shore near the present city of Monterey there once was a majestic live oak, its crest towering in solitary grandeur into the sky, its lowest branches lapped by the waters at high tide.

Many and varied were the scenes it must have witnessed during the centuries of its existence. But only surmise and conjecture can fill the morning of its life.

During the time that the tree's children were brown-skinned savages, it grew luxuriantly. In the splendor of its mature age, the white men came and chose to rest beside its rugged trunk, reveling in its far-flung screen of matted foliage. There they camped, prayed, solemnized, builded, departed.

But after the tree adopted for its wards the white-faced christians, and came to find its simple brown children harried out of their homes and lands, its leafage faded, its branches withered, and it died, grief-stricken.

Locked in its bed of concrete at the presidio chapel of Monterey, are its secrets, its dead hopes and its griefs, known only to its ancient comrades, the four winds and the whispering tides.

The old tree knew no people other than its brown children until in 1542 it saw three great white-winged ships rise over the watery horizon to the southward, move slowly and steadily across the waters, and sink themselves below the northern horizon.[46] They gave

---

[46] Rodriguez Cabrillo's expedition of 1542.

no sign of who or what they were, or whither bound. Yet the giant oak marveled at the sight of these monster boats and hoped that some day its brown children might sail in such.

Then for 60 more summers its foliage put forth and faded; for 60 winters gale-driven salt sprays dripped from its naked branches, and then through the bleak december twilight, looking out over the bay, it saw three more winged ships arise from the south. But these, instead of sweeping by, entered the harbor and there came to rest.

Again the tree remarked to itself the superiority of these strange ships to the frail tule canoes of its brown children. Truly the men who sailed in these must be superior beings. Yet it marveled at the daring of those men who would thus so audaciously defy the wrath of the storm gods.

Then came emaciated but stern-faced men, now rowing onto the beach, now greedily quenching their thirst in the near-by brook. This company of weary seamen gathered under the tree, where they fell upon their knees and prayed to their God for strength and courage to carry on the work they had to do. What men were they, the tree silently pondered, who, buffeted by gales, broken by suffering and privations, yet spoke of nothing but pressing on and on – to what clime? for what purpose? What great urge was driving these gaunt, resolute men to challenge and give battle again to the awful storm gods that its brown children so feared?

The leader of these men, Vizcaino, named the bay Monterey, in honor of the Conde de Monterey, viceroy of New Spain, and who, the tree understood, was an even mightier man than this Vizcaino who was obeyed by all his company. The oak, though unable to comprehend the motives of these white, bearded people, nevertheless was pleased to know that the waters that for centuries had laved its foot and whispered their lore to its leaves were to have the name of one who was a great man among his people.

The old oak approved these strangers, and it secretly began to wish that their arts and crafts might be imparted to the brown children whom it loved, and so bring to fulfillment the prophecy whispered to it long ago by the wind of the south; that on a day to come a new people would enter the land and teach the savages a better and safer life than now was theirs. Through the slow marching of the years the tree had hoped that it might live to see this prophecy brought to realization.

Why could not those white wayfarers leave their tents pitched on the sand and linger there, and teach their knowledge and their manner of living to the native children? Here were animals and fruits for food; here were fertile soils, water, wood, flowers.

But the old tree could not know that out on those ships were sick and dying comrades who must be turned back toward home; that up the coast were new lands and new peoples to be visited. No time for these men to delay longer than to muster strength to battle anew with storm and sea!

So, after a time, the tree saw the little fleet divide and sail away; and it felt grieved and abashed that its humble hospitality seemingly did not please the white men. The ships vanished, and the great oak was left again to shelter its simple native folk, and to ponder silently over the strange, suffering but indomitable men who had tarried for a while beneath its shade.

Now for 160 years the oak waited, watching land and sea faithfully for the return of the restless ones. It wanted them to come back. And that they would come back, the tree began to feel more and more assured for on their features, it remembered, there had been engraved a purpose, and this they would hand down to their children and their children's children, as an obligation. They would come back!

And so, after all these weary, slow-dragging years, they did come back – both by land and by sea.

And what was the old oak's gratification to find itself remembered and chosen by this generation for its rendezvous! A strange, persistent people, indeed!

But the tree learned, too, that the haggard, strained countenances of the former visitors were not characteristic of this people, for these white men demonstrated that they could laugh and shout for joy. The tree was pleased. It had been remembered; its hospitality had not been accepted and then scorned. Whatever it was that had kept these new friends away so long, they had remembered and had come back. And, whatever their purpose, it would be carried out here, and the tree would be a witness to it. The restless ones had come to stay.

Like their predecessors, the present company honored their God, and, after startling the wilderness with their bells, carried out their religious ceremonies. Then came the venerable Junipero Serra and planted beneath the wide-spreading oak a cross, marking the spot for the future mission of San Carlos which later was erected beside the tree. This towering tree and the towering soul of Serra must have possessed much in common.

Such thundering of cannon now shook the earth that the oak for a while felt apprehensive for its primitive children. What would result to them from the coming of the pale strangers? The tree so wanted them to be friends. It whispered its hope to the four winds, that its new wards would teach their superior arts and crafts to the old so that their privations and hardships might be lessened.

Then the tree found itself and the country round about taken possession of by the white commander, Portolá, in the name of Carlos III, king of Spain. So there was an even mightier man than the Monterey whom the tree remembered!

More white people came and with them their women and children. Now the old tree was eased. It knew that men bent on conquest and spoilation did not take their women and children with them. These people meant no harm to its brown children.

During the next half century, along the shores of Monterey Bay, the oak beheld amazing transformations, for the Spaniards clung to and executed their purpose – and it was the purpose for which the tree had longed and hoped.

By gifts, persuasion, and force, the timid brown folk were drawn from their squalid villages to the missions that were erected by the christians, and there they were taught the arts and ways of their white brethren. They came to discard feathers and the skins of animals for civilized garb; they became good farmers, herdsmen and craftsmen; their women learned how to weave, to dye cloth and make it into clothing, and to prepare foods that were both agreeable to the tongue and nourishing to the body. The tribes, instead of warring over miserable acorn groves, and dying of starvation, now possessed security and plenty.

But these changes came about slowly and, at times, tragically. The great tree, watching with pleasure the slow transformation of its children, whispered to the winds that it was no easy task to conquer a land in such manner. But, the tree also whispered, it would be an enduring conquest when completed!

And so it was that on the bank of Carmelo creek the San Carlos – first established beneath the mammoth oak in 1770 – became a thriving mission with great flocks and herds and many christian converts. From its place by the sea, the tree saw privations and hardships transmuted to plenty, and conflicts give way to peace. Its brown and its white children played beneath its shade, and brown and white men passed back and forth along the trail that led beside its trunk, carrying no weapons for killing, but going their ways in safety and assurance.

The tree listened to those who tarried and talked under its branches. Its leaves rustled with joy on hearing that not only here, but at nearly a score of other places along this great reach of seacoast, missions were being erected for the education and uplifting of the brown people.

The indefatigable Serra, in his journeys on foot among his missions, loved to rest a while under the cool protection of this oak. The old tree welcomed him, and felt grateful for the privilege of sheltering him. The two were friends, friends of few words and great understanding.

Only once during this half century did the oak droop in grief. In 1782 the beloved Serra, sick unto death, was borne beneath the tree on his way to the San Carlos mission, his favorite of them all. There he died, and there he was laid to rest. The old tree was comforted to see that his passing was sincerely mourned by both the brown and the white people. It hoped that when its life was ended, it might find a resting place near to that of its friend.

But the old tree could not foresee that in the very success of the missions lay their death. They had waxed prosperous, and the secular authorities were confronted by empty treasuries. So in 1830 an order for the secularization of the missions went forth.

And, as a result, from missions up and down the coast there drifted past the venerable tree bewildered, homeless neophytes, possessing a freedom unforeseen and unasked for.

The old oak's leaves, denied strength by a breaking heart, dropped untimely from the aged limbs. In a little while, the tree knew, the brown men, having no alternative, would seek old haunts, revive old habits, revert to the savagery from which they were so lately redeemed. There was sorrow ahead and the saddened tree was grateful that the waters of the bay were softly removing the soil from its roots.

It was grateful, too, that its good friend, Padre Serra, had not lived to witness the collapse of his sublime vision. Fortunate man! The tree had mourned his passing, but in the clarified sight that its grief had brought to it, it knew that the man was blest and that heaven had been merciful to him.

A little while, and the great tree which had stood sentinel over Monterey Bay for centuries sighed a brief farewell to its comrades, the four winds, and sank into the waiting arms of its other age-old comrade, the sea.

From some cause, the old tree was not carried out to sea with the tides. There it lay, majestic in death, year after year, its fiber gradually becoming mineralized through the infiltration of sea water.

Finally two men, who desired to render a service to later generations, procured a large scow, got grappling hooks upon the mighty trunk, and after many days' work succeeded in getting it ashore. It was loaded upon a specially-constructed conveyance, and taken to the presidio church in Monterey where, after being given a preservative treatment, it was reverently placed in a concrete bed that had been prepared for it. It has been rendered as enduring as granite by the preservative and it will be in existence long after all the other famous trees in this country have crumbled into dust.

In the mission church of San Carlos still repose the ashes of Junipero Serra, so the tree at last did find a resting place near to that of its friend.

The Pearls of Loreto

Young Fray Pedro Bonella gave an involuntary sigh
of relief as he entered the shaded precincts of Monterey.
He had trudged up the six miles from the Carmelo
mission that afternoon, and the sun had been hot. He
passed through a winding street, banked by its low,
one-story houses, to the seaward side of the town plaza
where he seated himself appreciatively on a rough
bench that he had espied beneath one of the great live
oak trees. Before him lay the broad Bay of Monterey,
reflecting in subdued tones the fading glory of sunset,
and from off its waters came a cool, fitful breeze which
Pedro sniffed gratefully.

As he became rested and refreshed, he began to take
note of his surroundings. In the squat houses that bor-
dered three sides of the plaza, the evening candles were
beginning to appear, and he saw a ship's lantern crawling up the staff on the battlemented tower of the presidio. From the far side of the plaza came discordant
chatter and laughter of people who were seeking a
social hour in this cool playground, and the contemplative mind of the young monk could not help con-
trasting the impotent noises and frettings of humanity
with the calm tranquillity of that vast sheet of water
that lay before him. His ascetic lips curved in a smile
of ironic resignation.

Presently, above the chatter of the people flocking

to the plaza, his ear caught the voices and laughter of a group of young men loitering near by.

"La Favorita must have her vanity satisfied," he heard one of them saying, "and her vanity reaches far. Is it not so, Vincento?"

The one addressed as Vincento – a handsome young hidalgo with the cold, predatory eye of an eagle – did not deign to reply nor even to look at his interlocutor, but continued to twist the ends of his black mustache reflectively.

The speaker went on:

"It is not enough that she has beauty and wealth exceeding that of any other señorita in California – no! She must possess pearls lovelier than those of any other woman in Monterey! A mere trifle, Señors – yes! A mere trifle! if one but knew where to find such pearls as the señorita demands!"

"And had the gold in one's purse," supplemented another. "Not one of us can offer her that which she has not. Ancestry? I told her that my ancestors fought under the Cid. She replied that hers had fought under Carlos Martel! You, Vincento, you possess a noble estate, but La Favorita possesses a still more magnificent one! Don Pablo, there – how huge a fortune has your father acquired through the Manila Galeón, Pablo? No matter – Ysabel has more! Now she demands the impossible, *diabla de las diablas!* She is like a babe crying for the moon!"

"So you still are writhing, Ramon?" laughed the one called Pablo. "Take the bruise like the rest of us who have writhed beneath her dainty silver slipper – with fortitude and philosophy!

"Santa Maria! but there are other señoritas as beautiful, and not so impossible to please, nor so difficult to find as would be the pearls that La Favorita demands as the price of her hand! For my part, gentilhombres, I would prefer a bride whose love may be given, but never purchased! Adios! I am off to church!"

The young men laughed and departed with light-hearted quips, leaving the unobserved priest alone with his meditations.

He remembered now having heard how Ysabel Herrera, known throughout California as La Favorita because of the lavish gifts nature and fortune had bestowed upon her, had announced to her suitors her marriage barter — a finer rope of pearls than was possessed by any other woman of California. Fray Pedro wondered why it should be that so many of those possessing every material blessing should be so deficient in spiritual and moral qualities.

Then he roused himself. Pablo's remark about proceeding to church reminded him that he was to assist at the service in the presidio chapel, and it was time he were going. Even as he rose the notes of the chapel bells came vibrating through the air, and the people began to saunter in pairs and groups toward the church.

Later in the evening, in the church, as Fray Pedro's contemplative eyes wandered over the departing worshipers, they fell upon the discomfited suitors of Ysabel Herrera, grouped together by a common bond of chagrin near the entrance. Pedro observed with amusement that while their attentions were conspicuously given to the neat, comely señoritas leaving the church, their glances strayed occasionally to the proud figure of La Favorita to see how she was taking their fine show of indifference to her presence.

Fray Pedro also observed that of these admirers only the handsome, daring Vincento de la Vega stood aloof and remained behind as the rest left the church. Then Pedro saw him accompany Ysabel and her duenna as they departed.

When all were gone, the altar put in order, and the candles extinguished, Pedro noted that it still was early in the night, so he decided to return to his cool bench in the plaza for an hour's meditation and to refresh himself with the clean, cool sea breeze. So, bidding his fellow priest good-night, he made his way thither.

He was surprised to find the bench occupied by three persons. One, a plump, elderly woman, leaned somnolently against the tree; the other two, a man and woman, sat close together and talked in low tones.

Fray Pedro was about to retire when the man's words caught his ear, and for the second time that night he became an eavesdropper – this time a voluntary one.

"You shall have them, Ysabel," the man was declaring. "The finest pearls in all New Spain! I doubt that any royal throat of Europe is adorned with gems as magnificent! I have seen them! A wonderful, double rope, Ysabel – worth thrice a king's ransom! You shall have them; I swear it!"

Ysabel's mellow contralto voice replied, incredulously,

"Vincento! You must be beside yourself to promise me such a gift and to pledge yourself to it! Where are such pearls to be found, outside the pope's own treasury?"

"Ha, Where? What matters where, *inamorita,* so long as I promise them to you? A few weeks, Ysabel, and they shall be yours! Until then, incline your heart to me and await my return. I will make haste, and I will return with the pearls that shall make you mine!"

Fray Pedro cautiously withdrew without having been seen. At Vincento's words, "a wonderful, double rope of pearls, worth thrice a king's ransom," the look on Pedro's face changed from one of contemptuous amusement to one of alarmed concern.

For he could have answered Ysabel's question, "Where are such pearls to be found?" He knew where was the only double rope of pearls in all Spain's dominions that was worth thrice the ransom of a king. He knew of the indian tribe that for two generations had been employed in the pearl fisheries of the Gulf of California; he knew how every exceptionally large, perfect pearl had been taken, one by one, to a certain place until, after half a century, enough had been accumulated to form that glorious double rope of matchless magnificence.

But after a while he began to feel some doubt as to his suspicion. It might be, he reflected, that Vincento's promise was but a boast designed to draw Ysabel's favorable attention to him. Enamored men ever have recklessly promised more than they could pay.

Nevertheless, Pedro determined to keep this man under surveillance for he knew him to be very daring, and he had heard that he was unscrupulous as well.

The next day it was learned that Vincento had departed southward on his best mount. It also was learned that Fray Pedro, who had paid a hurried call on the *padre superior* at Carmelo, had secured an indefinite leave of absence and also had departed on a swift andalusian horse.

Vincento's departure, being nothing out of the ordinary, roused no comment; but it certainly was unprecedented that a franciscan friar should either be in haste or be so worldly as to travel on a valuable, spirited horse.

Pedro's route led southward through sand deserts and mountainous wastes, and sometimes along the seashore; but it was an easy, well-traveled trail and the missions scattered along it — each one a great, refreshing oasis — were at the farthest only a day's journey apart.

Pedro traveled rapidly. He stopped for the night at the San Miguel mission. There he found Vincento, and the suspicion that lay in Pedro's mind was strengthened by Vincento's evasion when questioned discreetly as to the object of his journey.

The next morning Fray Pedro, who himself was an early riser, learned that Vincento had risen before him and already had departed. Fray Pedro made a hasty breakfast and set out in pursuit. Before noon he caught sight of Vincento's white horse in the distance ahead.

Thereafter he kept himself informed as to the man's progress. Mounted travelers were encountered occasionally, and from these, as well as through inquiries at the missions and settlements along the route, Pedro knew at all times about how far Vincento was ahead and where he spent each night. Vincento himself apparently was entirely oblivious of the fact that he was being trailed. At the various missions where he stopped for the night he always stated, so Pedro learned, that he was on his way to San Diego on a special commission.

On and on they proceeded. Five days after leaving

Monterey they reached San Diego, the southernmost settlement in California Alta. But instead of tarrying there, Vincento kept on southward over the trail leading down through California Baja with Fray Pedro still inexorably following.

Down over the long trail through the peninsula went the two, Pedro keeping two or three miles behind. He always observed where Vincento stopped for the night and then, going on to the next mission or village, there waited, concealed, until Vincento passed by the next morning.

In succession they reached and left behind the missions of San Vincente, Santa Maria, Santa Gertrudis, San Pablo, Santa Magdalena.

At dusk on the evening of the seventh day after passing through San Diego, they entered the ranches and fields belonging to the mission of Nuestra Señora de Loreto. Screened by the trees and orchards, Fray Pedro cautiously drew up closer, and after a while, when Vincento dismounted, Pedro did the same and led his horse out of the roadway, picketing it. He then followed on foot. He observed that Vincento, after concealing his horse in a secluded glade, went on and found a hiding place for himself in some shrubbery near the road to the mission church. Pedro concluded that the man intended to wait there until it was completely dark before going farther with his project.

Pedro struck a roundabout course through the growing crops, to avoid being seen by Vincento, and fifteen minutes later he was hammering at the gate of the convento. The venerable *padre superior* admitted him.

"Enter, now, and rest, my son," said the old man, after the greetings. "You are weary, and it appears from the dust on your clothing that you have come a long way. After you have bathed and eaten, we will then hear your business."

"My business cannot wait, Padre," answered Pedro. "It is urgent. Afterward I can rest, but not now."

He then revealed his suspicions of Vincento, and told how he had followed him all the way down from Monterey, and how the man even then was concealed in the shrubbery on the mission grounds.

"I know it appears incredible to you, Padre," concluded Pedro, "but this Vincento de la Vega is a young man devoid of virtues and an unscrupulous one. He will hesitate at nothing."

"Very well," answered the old man as he arose from his seat, "we can easily circumvent him. You will remain here and rest," he added, as Pedro arose to accompany him. "You are weary from having ridden all day. I will return within the half hour." The old priest departed.

The half hour passed, and he had not returned. When the interval had lengthened to an hour, Pedro, who had been growing more and more uneasy, summoned an indian servant and the two set out for the church to find what was delaying the *padre superior*.

Two weeks later there was a grand ball given at the presidio in Monterey. This *baile* had been arranged to honor the officers of a British man-of-war that lay in the harbor, but there had been some unfortunate friction with the port officials and the British officers remained aloof in anger, and were preparing to sail at dawn the next morning.

All the socially elite of the province had been invited. Most of them were present and the great hall in the presidio had been especially decorated for the occasion.

The revelry was just beginning when the oaken door was swung open and Ysabel Herrera, flushed with triumph and gloriously radiant in a magnificent double festoon of pearls, entered on the arm of Vincento de la Vega.

There was a gasp of astonished admiration, and then a surge of the guests toward the triumphant pair. Superlative exclamations flew through the air, and Ysabel was the focus of a hundred pairs of worshipful eyes and an equal number of wildly envious ones.

Then there came shoving his way roughly through the massed throng a travel-stained, breathless young franciscan priest – Fray Pedro Bonella – his eyes blazing with rage.

"Murderer! Desecrator! Accursed!" he screamed, pointing a quivering finger at Vincento. "Seize him! SEIZE HIM!"

The guests stood gaping in amazement and alarm and the men nearest Pedro, thinking him suddenly gone insane, laid hold of him and tried to thrust him back. He struggled to free himself, and finally gasped hoarsely,

"He murdered the padre of the Loreto! He stripped those pearls from the holy statue of the Mother of God! Seize him!"

Horrified, the guests turned. But Vincento and Ysabel had fled through the door, closing it behind them. Pedro tore through the dazed crowd and flung himself at the door. It was bolted from the other side!

"Pursue them! Are you all daft?" yelled the man. He hurled his weight against the door and the bolt splintered from the wood. Some of the men, who now were recovering their wits, ran out with Pedro. They hastily searched the other rooms, but found no one. Then they rushed out to the presidio gateway.

"Did a man and woman pass through here?" shouted Pedro to the sentry at the gate.

"Yes – yes!" stammered the bewildered guard. "They took the road to the harbor!"

Snatching the carbine from the amazed sentry, Pedro dashed away, followed by half the throng, their man-hunting instincts now fully aroused. They ran on toward the beach, and there, where the road ahead led over the crest of a hill, they saw the forms of the two fugitives sharply silhouetted against the moonlit sky. Clearly they were fleeing to the protection of the British ship in the harbor, and it was too late to intercept them!

Pedro stopped instantly, took a careful aim, and fired. The man was seen to fling up his arms, stumble, and then disappear from view.

As the pursuers raced shouting up over the brow of the hill, they stopped short, awed into sudden silence, their atavistic lust for killing stricken from them. For there on her knees was Ysabel, her hysterical words of endearment and grief mingling with the horrible sobs of her stricken lover.

The sobs ceased, and the man's head fell back. Then, before any of the onlookers could understand what she was about, much less move to prevent her, Ysabel struggled to her feet, still embracing the body of her lover, and flung herself and him over the precipice into the sea!

Pedro was the first to speak.

"God's pity on her!" he exclaimed, softly. "How much nobler her death than his!"

The body of Ysabel was recovered, but the wonderful pearls of Our Lady of Loreto never were found. It may be that Ysabel, horrified by Vincento's crime, hurled them away from her during her flight. Or possibly they were lost in the sea. It is said that search still is occasionally made for them to this day.

The Mexicans, facile at pointing morals, declare that the death of Vincento without the ministrations of the church was a visitation of divine vengeance; that the fate of Ysabel was a similar visitation for having incited him to the crime; and that the famous pearls were made to disappear that they might never again be a temptation to any man.

Others, however, will note and remember but the one thing – that however tawdry her life, in her death Ysabel Herrera was sublime.

Father Magin's Alameda

One of the most beautiful spots in the world is the Santa Clara valley in California. It takes its name from the Spanish mission that was established there in 1777, although the little stream that courses through the valley is called the Guadalupe.

Only a memorial cross now marks the spot where this industrial mission was first built and dedicated to Madre Santa Clara de Asis. A religious college today occupies the later site of the mission.

Of the two franciscan padres designated to take charge of the Santa Clara in 1777, one, Fray José Viador, served until the secularization and consequent abandonment of the mission in 1833; the other, Fray Magín Catala, served until his death in 1830.

These two men, while strikingly in contrast to each other, worked harmoniously together and possessed an affection for each other that was beautiful and enduring.

Fray Magín, one of the most remarkable missionaries of the whole California field, was frail, ascetic, and saintly. He was credited during his lifetime with prophetic powers and to his soubriquet, El Santo (The Saint) that his austere life had earned for him was added El Profeto (The Prophet). It is claimed by the descendants of the people he served that he correctly foretold the loss of California to Spain, its subsequent seizure by the United States, the discovery of gold, the coming of the Americans, the future greatness of the city of San Francisco, and even the destruction of that city by earthquake and fire. Fray Magín possessed a wholesome fear of women, and believed they were the favorite instrument of the devil in encompassing the destruction of men's souls.

Fray José was a man of large stature and brawny, athletic build. At one time he soundly thrashed three husky Indians who set upon him, then lectured them severely upon the sin of attacking a priest and the unwisdom of attempting to whip him and thereby made the three Indians his faithful friends for life.

Fray José was also inclined to be a bit worldly, and created some mild scandal among his fellow missionaries by wearing a straw hat, by his cultivated taste in wines (of which, however, he never tasted to excess) and because he had a carriage built for his use in visiting outlying indian communities that were under the spiritual care of the mission.

Fray Magín slept on the floor of his cell, with an adobe brick for a pillow, but it is impossible to imagine Fray José doing so if a more comfortable couch were to be had.

Yet the two men, each recognizing the excellent qualities of the other, were close friends and allies for more than half a century, and they alone developed the Santa Clara mission until it was one of the three highest in point of productiveness and the one highest in the number of its indian adherents.

Soon after the mission of Santa Clara was founded, the Spanish town of San José was established, three miles up the Guadalupe river from the mission. For many years this town had no church of its own and the people there were obliged to travel the three miles to and from the mission in order to attend mass. – C.H.

———

Padre Magín entered the mission refectory and sat down to his customary evening meal of gruel, wearily and with a suppressed groan.

He had spent the day with sick people in the town of San José, three miles from his own mission of Santa Clara. In spite of his pain, and the burning sun, he had tramped the three miles both ways.

For many years, Padre Magín had been afflicted with rheumatism. Now his face, lined with suffering, appeared to be that of a man much older than his 35 years. But the little prayer on the man's lips was as constant as his ailment – and as much a part of himself – giving him strength and courage to fulfill his many daily tasks without complaint.

As Padre Magín sank into his chair, Padre José looked up from the meal he was finishing, his eyes glistening with sympathy for the weaker man.

"Your suffering and your weariness trouble me, Brother," he said anxiously. "Let me bring you a little wine."

Padre Magín shook his head slowly.

"It is but a touch of the sun," he explained. "It will pass. But, Brother, as I was walking through the heat today, I felt a compassion for the christians of San José who must endure the sun for three miles when they wish to hear our services. It must be very hard on the women and children; and I desire very much that all the children of San José be brought within the fold of the church. I have thought –" he paused, hesitatingly.

"What is it that you have thought, Brother?" inquired Padre José after a few moments.

"It is this. I had the idea that if some of the poplar trees that line the streams up in the hills were rooted along the lane between this mission and San José, it would make the long walk more comfortable for the people of San José who come here for mass and confession."

Padre José seemed to be turning this matter over in his mind while his companion finished his tardy and frugal supper. Then the two retired to the open air in the cooling twilight and sat down together.

"Now let us talk about that lane as you would have it, Brother," began Padre José, the practical. "Your idea is not at all unfeasible. Most of our Indians now have little to do, and will have little to do until the crops are ready to be harvested. Why cannot we set them to work digging up the trees from the arroyos in the hills and transplanting them along the lane?"

"But, Brother," answered Padre Magín, "we shall have to wait until winter. The trees would die if taken up and replanted at this season."

Padre José smiled indulgently. "You are a good teacher and preceptor for our Indians, Brother," he replied, "but it is little that you know about trees. Prune off most of their branches, and they will live and grow even at this season of the year."

Soon the attention of the people of San José was attracted toward work that was being done on the lane running southwestward to the mission. Padre Magín had set his indian workmen to bringing in poplar trees and setting them in a double row on each side of the lane. Down from the little hill valleys came lumbering carts drawn by oxen and mules, dragging the uprooted poplars and, as though these would not suffice, squads of muscular Indians with rawhide ropes were stolidly tugging along, pulling other trees down the arroyos and into the three-mile lane. The Indians liked Padre Magín and they worked willingly for him.

Then the good padre conceived another idea. He, in spite of his infirmities, was a lover of the open air. Why not erect along this new *alameda,* the fourteen stations of the cross, so that the religious ceremony known as *via crucis* (the way of the cross) could be carried out in the open, and so simulate more closely the original tragic way of the cross that had been enacted in Jerusalem eighteen centuries before?

It was a novel idea, never before put into practice in all christendom, although it has since been done a number of times. Padre Magín proceeded at once to put it into execution, and the fourteen stations were erected at intervals of about 400 feet, beginning at the mission and extending over a mile along the *alameda.*

An *asequia* was dug from the little Guadalupe river to the *alameda* and there divided, one branch going down each side of the road, for the watering of the trees during periods of dry weather.

Finally, the rows of trees extended the entire three miles to the village of San José. The last tree was planted by Padre Magín himself, with simple but appropriate ceremonies, in the presence of a large body of Spaniards and Indians, all of whom now looked forward to the day when their *alameda* between village and church would be blessed with shade.

The trees grew rapidly, and within ten or twelve years formed a beautiful archway. The road became famed throughout California as *la alameda de Santa Clara,* by which name it still is known. The trees converted the road into a thoroughfare so attractive that mission-going became very popular with the San Joséans, and the *alameda* became a favorite promenade for the townspeople on sundays, feast days, and evenings. On every friday, and also on holy days, the way of the cross was enacted by Padre Magín and his Indians, carrying at the head of their procession the large crucifix belonging to the church.

Thirty-three years had elapsed since Padre Magín's arrival at Santa Clara, and the mission had prospered. The padre now was an old man and, too infirm to occupy his pulpit, he preached to his congregation seated in a chair by the altar rail.

By and by strange tales of dark and mysterious doings on the *alameda* began to be whispered among the people of San José. Horses had taken fright at things unseen and had run away, throwing their riders. One horseman had been killed. An Indian had been found dead under the trees with no marks on his body. Strange figures had been seen darting in and out among the trunks; people told of screams and groans rending the air. The *alameda* was entirely deserted by the birds that formerly had nested and sung there. New stories of strange and terrible sights and sounds along the *alameda* arose nearly every day. People became hesitant about traveling along it even in broad daylight, and only a very daring or foolhardy man would venture to traverse it after nightfall for it was at night that its demoniacally supernatural aspect became manifest.

Padre Magín all this while was wondering why his white congregation was falling off. He still exhorted them as vigorously as ever; he still pointed out to them the benefits accruing to exemplary conduct. He thought for a while that it was because he, owing to his infirmities, no longer visited the San Joséans in person, but he considered this the more reason why they should come to him.

When, after a while, the whites in his congregation had dwindled to a mere handful, he decided something must be seriously the matter and, meeting one of the few men of San José who still came to church, he detained him long enough to make some inquiries. Thus was the unfortunate condition revealed to him.

"The *alameda* has become the resort of demons, Padre," this man assured the amazed priest. "I have not seen these demons myself, but numerous people have seen them, they have heard them and have come under their baneful influence.

"There is Pedro Mateo, for example. Only two nights gone, when he was returning in the early morning before daybreak from a gaming party at the rancho del Toro Azul, he saw the fiery-red eyes of a shape from the pit glaring at him from the shrubbery ahead. Whereas Pedro unfortunately was somewhat under the influence of the wine he had drunk, the sight of those malignant eyes sobered him on the instant and silenced the song he was singing, and he fled across field and *vega* until he fell, exhausted, at the door of the *alcalde* in San José. That this is true, the *alcalde* himself will testify.

"The *alameda* is accursed, Padre. It has become the haunt of fiends and of horrible shapes from the pit. I carry my crucifix in my hand whenever I traverse it, and recite my Pater Nosters and Ave Marias continually until I reach the end. For this reason, I believe, the demons have not molested me."

The following sunday Padre Magín announced to his congregation that he had been informed by a revelation that satan, enraged because the church had drawn away most of his followers in San José, had sent his hellish hosts to haunt the *alameda* and so prevent the people from coming to church; and that these fiends, emboldened by their success, were even then planning the destruction of both the mission and San José by destroying their crops and so starving them into death or flight. As evidence of the truth of this, the padre pointed out to them that from no apparent cause the yield of crops at both San José and the mission was much smaller than the year before.

He concluded by informing the startled people that it was his duty, as their spiritual father, to make an effort to drive out the unclean spirits that were haunting the beautiful *alameda*.

He dismissed his congregation, bidding them go home and pray for him in his hour of conflict with the powers of darkness. Instead the alarmed neophytes gathered about him, begging that he attempt no such perilous task, while the Spaniards and Padre José joined in urging him to return to the convento and rest.

"You are too ill and frail for such a superhuman trial, Brother," urged Padre José.

"I must go," declared Padre Magín resolutely. "You will take me to the *alameda,* Brother, and leave me there. I must drive out these demons before they destroy my mission and my people. My own life does not matter."

Seeing that he was determined, Padre José and an

Indian, one on each side, supported him as he made his way unsteadily to the head of the *alameda*. The entire congregation of whites and Indians followed, apprehensively, until they neared the end of the lane. There they halted, spellbound and fearful, and watched.

"Let me go," said Padre Magín, when they reached the lane.

"But, Brother," protested Padre José, "you will fall. You can not stand alone."

"Let me go," repeated the other, "and have no fear for me. Wait here for me."

Padre José and the Indian released the man and stepped back. With his head bowed and his frame trembling, Padre Magín stood a moment, praying for strength to walk just once more.

Then he stumbled forward, recovered himself, and to the astonishment of the watchers lifted his shoulders and walked easily up the tree-embowered *alameda*. On and on he walked, and presently began reciting the exorcism for evil spirits.

Suddenly the watching crowd were startled by a loud cry of agony, as of many voices, coming from the *alameda;* then came a horrible howling, cursing, and screaming that made the terrified watchers blanch from fear. Then followed a chorus of unearthly groans from the retreating demons; a great cloud of dust arose over the poplars and the air seemed charged with sulphurous fumes.

After the dust had cleared, the people, their anxiety for their padre overcoming their fears, rushed to the head of the lane and there they saw their beloved Padre Magín returning to them in triumph; the birds were coming from all directions to the trees, making the air vibrant with their joyous music. All ran forward to meet the padre.

"The demons are gone! They will trouble us no more!" he cried, then fainted just as Padre José's strong arms swept him into a brotherly embrace.

Padre Magín walked no more. But the *alameda* was saved. It once more was beautiful and wholesome. It became a parade ground for the San Joséans, whereon they again displayed their silks and velvets, and journeyed to and from church without fear.

And so the old *alameda* has survived to this day. Only a few of the original poplars remain, but the rows have been reset from time to time with eucalyptus, elder, locust, and willow trees, and the thoroughfare is still as beautiful as ever.

Fray Magín was greatly loved by whites and Indians alike. Chase and Saunders, in *The California padres and their missions,* have this to say of the old padre's death:

There is a touch of poetry about his death. During his last illness, there came an evening when he called to him two faithful Indians and, telling them that he should die at dawn, asked them to remain with him during the night.

"Watch the sky," he bade them, "and when the morning star appears, tell me."

They did as he directed, and when they beheld what they watched for, they went with the news to his bedside.

"Padre, the morning star has risen."

"Then, my children," he said, "please call Padre José to come and pray over me."

Padre José hastened in, and, as he recited the prayers for the dying, El Santo's spirit passed beyond the veil.

The Padre of the San Luis Rey

The San Luis Rey, founded in 1798, always was in the front rank industrially and at the crest of its career was the most prosperous of all. Architecturally, it is the queen of the California missions. Duhaut-Cilly, who visited San Luis Rey in 1827, gives this picture of it:

> After a jaunt of an hour and a half from the seashore we found before us, on a piece of rising ground, the superb buildings of the mission San Luis Rey, whose glittering whiteness was flashed back to us by the first rays of the sun. At that distance . . . this edifice, of a very beautiful model, supported on its numerous pillars, had the aspect of a palace. . . Instinctively, I stopped my horse to gaze alone, for a few minutes, on the beauty of this sight.

At that time, the mission owned four great ranches, the hills and vales of which were dotted with nearly 30,000 sheep and an equal number of cattle. Its farms were producing 13,000 bushels of wheat alone annually. Sixteen beeves and 40 sheep were slaughtered each week to provide meat for its population of nearly 3,000 christian Indians. The mission not only was self-supporting, but it sold cargoes of merchandise to English and American traders; it owned property, aside from its ranches, worth $200,000; it was lending money to the governments of Mexico and California.

This wealth had been created by and belonged to the Indians of the San Luis Rey; and it all was the result of the faith, energy, ability, and courage of one man, Padre Antonio Peyri. He had been placed in charge of the mission when it first was founded. He was its architect, it promoter, its organizer, its manager. He had companion priests at times, but they came and departed. Peyri remained. He was in charge of the mission from the time it was founded in 1798 until his departure in 1831 – a third of a century.

This splendid industrial establishment was more than his life's work. It was a living, pulsating part of the man himself. San Luis Rey was Peyri's soul made manifest.

But rebellion was in the air and the star of Spain was sinking. Her banners were being furled on half a score of frontiers where they had flown for two and three centuries. Into the seats of the Spanish grandees who had governed through those centuries, revolution placed native rulers hostile to everything that savored of the Spanish regime. These new rulers looked upon the accumulated wealth and the rich lands of the missions and wrote their end.

Padre Antonio Peyri was apprehensive of this move, for rumors of it had been coming up through California Baja for several years. Peyri viewed it as a helpless father views the tide that creeps up to engulf his equally helpless children.

One morning in december, 1831, his personal servant approached him with a troubled countenance.

"Padre, it has come," he said, simply.

Moonlight and deep shadows lay upon the court of the San Luis Rey, adding to its beauty their element of mystery. The Indians were sleeping in their quarters. The evening service in the church had been heard with more attention than usual, for the congregation had

CHURCH OF SAN LUIS REY

been told by visiting Indians that they would be sent away from their mission before long, and Padre Antonio had seemed strangely troubled as he urged them, with tears in his eyes and a new intensity to his voice, to remember and obey his teachings. But the peaceful night had coaxed them to put away their misgivings until the morrow, when they could go to their padre and tell him their fears – and now all was still in the settlement.

Presently, stealthy footsteps sounded along the cloister and then a long-gowned figure appeared, moving along next to the wall, out of the moonlight. It stopped.

"Manuelito!"

"I come, Padre Antonio," answered a small voice in a stage whisper, as an indian boy slipped from a patch of deep shade to the priest's side.

"Are the others ready, my son?"

"Si!"

"Then watch my window. When the light goes out, we will meet you. Remember!"

"Si, Padre." The boy melted again into the shadows.

With a deep, tremulous sigh, the old priest moved on toward his room. He knew the boy would station himself in a tree, near the edge of the settlement, and watch for the signal.

In his room Padre Antonio lighted a candle and placed it near the window. Then he dropped wearily to a rude bench.

How precious were these last moments in his austere but friendly old room! Across his mind's eye there drifted scenes memorable in his life and in mission history. On this ground in 1798 he had assisted with the ceremonies attending the founding of the mission.

He remembered the vibrant tones of Presidente Lasuen's voice, as that good man spoke to loyal neophytes and inquisitive gentiles – Lasuen, his friend, who now for 30 years had been sleeping in the holy ground of Carmel.

He recalled his pride in this new church that had been erected in 1801 to meet the needs of his fast-growing colony of converts. In 1816 he had ministered to the Indians at Pala, aiding them to build their own church and instructing them in the tilling of the soil and the rearing of livestock. What hours of rejoicing he had known because of the impression his religion had made upon the untutored savages!

The chubby brown children whom he had taken into his arms and told the story of the Christ-child, a third of a century before, were parents and grandparents now, but his devoted adherents still. They in turn had brought their children and grandchildren to their Padre Antonio for baptism and instruction.

Three generations of faithful followers!

Peyri had begun this work when he was a young man. Now he was old. The mission was his life blood. There, in the distance, stretched its great, prosperous ranches. Here, silently sleeping, was his colony of 3000 civilized, industrious Indians. These brown people had trusted him; they had followed his guidance and accepted his reproofs without a murmur; they loved him. Yonder through his window he could see the now silent, deserted plaza where his indian band of 40 pieces played in the evenings. There, in a tile of the pavement – he could see the mark in the bright moonlight – was the imprint of an indian child's foot, impressed there while the tile was yet soft. That child now was a man with children of his own.

So Peyri in his bare cell passed his work in review before him, and he felt that he could not trust himself to take leave of his flock. For 33 years he had devoted himself to the upbuilding of this institution. To deliver this trust now into the hands of the secular government, to permit his children to turn back to savagery, was more than his spirit could bear.

But the orders had come for the mission San Luis Rey to be yielded up. The inconquerable Peyri was conquered.

A tap at his door startled him.

He stepped out into the night and was joined by the man he was awaiting, Governor Victoria, an exiled official who had sought rest in the peaceful tranquillity of the mission – Victoria, the last of the swashbuckling governors of Spanish blood, exiled for having championed the cause of the missionary teachers.

"Let us make haste, Padre," whispered Victoria. "If your Indians miss you, there will be trouble. Shall I blow out the light? Our signal —"

"Yes – yes – " answered Peyri, chokingly. "Blow out the light."

Who can know what the extinguishing of this candle meant to the old priest – what it symbolized to him?

Victoria put out the light and the two made their way to the edge of the settlement, screening themselves in the shadows. There they found four indian youths waiting, tense with excitement.

"Do you still wish to go with me to Spain, my children?" Peyri asked them.

The boys closed in upon him and begged to be taken wherever he was going.

The padre blessed them and sent them ahead to bring the horses they had concealed farther up the road.

The boys returned, and all mounted. Peyri could not trust himself to take a backward look at that moment.

But after half an hour, on a hilltop that afforded a last view of his mission, he asked Victoria and three of the boys to go on, saying that he would rejoin them presently. The one boy who remained with him had been his assistant in the church.

Then the old priest, shaken by great sobs, dismounted and, falling to his knees and with his face toward the massed buildings that gleamed white in the distant moonlight, implored God to guard and protect his abandoned people.

Now he remounted, but sat staring toward the noble majesty of his fated mission. The darkness had deepened, but still the outlines of the buildings, every line of which was known and loved by the padre, stood out clearly in the night and etched themselves upon his memory.

So long he remained that Victoria came riding back to join him.

"Come, Padre," he urged. "You are going home! Home to Barcelona!"

"I am going into exile, Señor," replied Peyri huskily. "I go into exile! My home is here! I was present when my mission was founded, a third of a century ago! How well I remember! We baptized 54 children that first day."

"Mi madre!" exclaimed the indian boy at his side.

"Yes. Your mother was one of those 54 infants."

Victoria could not understand. He was in sympathy with the missions and the missionaries, but – a man sorrowing because he was going home! An infinite gulf separated the two men.

With tears streaming down his broad, heavy face, Padre Antonio turned his horse again toward San Diego, where a ship was awaiting him.

The next morning while the priest stood on the deck of the vessel that was to take him back to Spain, he saw, racing on ponies toward San Diego, several hundred Indians. The native boy beside him exclaimed, joyfully, "Our people come! Take you back!"

In the settlement the alarm was sounded. The people there saw only that a large band of Indians was approaching furiously. For a moment Padre Antonio's heart froze in fear that his Indians would be fired upon. Calling to the men on the shore, he made them understand that these were friendly Indians from San Luis Rey. This word was rapidly passed to the frightened people and the alarm subsided.

But the people gathered and looked on in absorbed interest. On came the shouting, excited throng – right down to the water's edge. Padre Antonio's people, having learned that he had gone from them, were here to take him back – forcibly, if necessary. They begged, implored, shrieked. Just as the vessel weighed anchor, some of the brown men, seeing it move, plunged into the sea and swam vigorously after it. On shore all was confusion, a babbling, screaming tumult.

But all became stilled as Padre Antonio lifted his arms and, in a broken voice, blessed his flock. His eyes rested affectionately upon them while the ship bore him on toward the horizon and a half-forgotten Spain.

In the chapel of the San Luis Rey there was a picture of Peyri, representing him surrounded by indian children. For many years the Indians continued to hope for his return and to pray to this picture, imploring him to come back to them. When reproved for addressing their prayers to a mortal man, they replied simply that it was better to pray to a saint they had known in the flesh than to those they had only heard about.

In 1841 some of Peyri's Indians were living, in poverty, at one of the former mission ranches – the ranch of Los Flores. In that year a Captain Mofras visited this ranch. An old Indian approached him and said, interrogatively,

"Señor, they tell me you are from Spain."

"So I am," replied Mofras.

"Did you see our Padre Antonio?"

"No; Padre Antonio Peyri is dead."

"Señor," replied the Indian reprovingly, "that padre does not die!"

Five years later the few Indians, who still clung to the abandoned mission in the hope and belief that somehow their Padre Antonio would return, were expelled by United States troops who needed the mission for use as a barracks. So ended the story of Peyri of the San Luis Rey.

Concha's Lover

On the baptismal records of the old Dolores church in San Francisco is an entry dated february 26, 1791, recording the baptism and christening on that day of Maria de la Concepción Marcela Arguello, daughter of Don José Arguello, captain of the royal presidio and commandant of the port of San Francisco.

Under a date 66 years later, on the records of the convent at Benicia, California, is found the following entry.

In the convent of Saint Catherine of Sienna, at Benicia, California, died Sister Maria Dominica, december 23, 1857. She was buried on christmas eve, dressed in her white habit as a nun. . . After the solemn requiem service was ended, the last benediction of the catholic church was pronounced over her mortal remains, *requiescat in pace!* dismissing a tired soul out of the storms of life into the divine tranquillity of death. . .

On april 5, 1806, the Count Nikolai Petrovitch Rezanof, commanding the Russian ship Juno, approached the Golden Gate of San Francisco Bay. He had come down from Alaska, seeking food for the straitened Russian colony there, of which it appears he was in charge. The crew of his ship also was on very short rations, and suffering from scurvy.

At that time it was contrary to Spanish law for any vessel flying a foreign flag to enter San Francisco Bay. Rezanof was aware of this law, but his colony was in desperate need. As he sailed in past the fort at the entrance of the bay, he was challenged by the sentry:

"What ship goes there?"

"The Russian ship, Juno!" shouted Rezanof, in reply.

"Release your anchor!"

"Yes, sir!" answered Rezanof, at the same time instructing his men to pretend to be releasing the anchor. They also pretended to be having difficulty in letting it go and meanwhile the ship was drifting on into the bay. When well within, Rezanof anchored.

He then sent two of his officers ashore in a boat to ascertain the temper of the Spaniards. They were met by Don José Arguello, commandant of the port, and were courteously treated.

It happened that circumstances favored Rezanof. The Spanish officials had received information of a Russian ship that was making an exploring tour of the world and they had been instructed to show the foreign explorers every courtesy should they appear in California waters.

So Rezanof himself went ashore, and Arguello, believing him to be the Russian explorer, took him into his own home as a guest.

Rezanof now, without explaining that his was not the exploring ship and without revealing the starving condition of his crew, began negotiations for exchanging the cargo of manufactured goods, that his ship carried, for foodstuffs.

But here he encountered another Spanish law, which forbade the exchange of foodstuffs for goods carried by foreign ships.

The governor, Arrillaga, had come up from Monterey to greet the supposed distinguished Russian explorer, and Arguello put up to him the matter of provisioning Rezanof's ship. Arrillaga was a great stickler for the letter of the law, so he hesitated and procrastinated for several days. He was about to stretch a point and yield, as a matter of courtesy, when Rezanof made a false move. Thinking to further his cause by appealing to the sympathy of the governor, he revealed the facts that his was not the exploring ship and that his crew, as well as the colony in Alaska, were in a starving condition.

This had an effect opposite to what Rezanof had desired. Arrillaga had received no instructions to extend any courtesies to foreign trading ships, so now he flatly refused to permit the exchange of food for Rezanof's cargo of merchandise.

At this point a disturbing factor in the form of a charming young woman entered the situation.

Concepción Arguello, the daughter of the commandant of the port, was the acknowledged beauty of the province of Alta California. Von Langsdorff, surgeon and naturalist of Rezanof's ship, said of Concepción that she was "lively and animated, with sparkling, love-inspiring eyes, beautiful teeth, pleasing and expressive features, a fine form, and a thousand other charms, yet perfectly simple and artless."

And Langsdorff was an old man. Is it any marvel, then, that the young Count Rezanof should be completely conquered by the black eyes of the Spanish beauty? And she had as completely lost her heart to this big, blonde Russian who, after the manner of men, had pictured to her the splendors of the Russian capital and the social advantages she would enjoy there as the Countess Rezanof.

Concepción's parents objected to the engagement of

the two because of Concepción's youth – she was only fifteen – and because Rezanof was not a catholic, but their real reason probably was that they did not want to lose Concepción entirely for, if she married Rezanof, likely they never would see her again. But the girl had a will of her own, and Rezanof would not yield. In the end the resolution of the lovers prevailed, the parents gave their consent, and a formal betrothal was announced.

The governor continued to remain unmoved by the arguments of Don José Arguello who, as Rezanof's prospective father-in-law, now was zealously championing his cause. So Concepción herself went to the governor and delivered an eloquent plea for her fiancé's starving crew and colony. And finally Arrillaga, to get rid of her and silence her importunities, gave a grumbling consent that the vessel be provisioned.

Concepción herself carried the glad news to Rezanof. The exchange of Russian goods for California foodstuffs was promptly effected, and Rezanof prepared to sail immediately for Alaska. He informed Concepción that after he had relieved the hungry colony, he would proceed directly to Saint Petersburg to secure the consent of the czar to his marriage and to arrange for turning over his colony to some other manager.

Concepción accompanied him to his ship, and there the two lovers said goodbye. It was a long, long way to Rezanof's home in Saint Petersburg, the overland journey itself being about 3000 miles, but he promised to make haste and to return for his bride before another year was sped.

So Concepción returned to the shore, and the Russian ship sailed outbound through the Golden Gate. Con-

CONCEPCIÓN ARGUELLO
Posed by Miss Christina V. Delgado, Santa Fe, New Mexico

cepción watched until it was completely swallowed up in the haze that obscured the horizon.

Probably no premonitory warnings troubled her soul as she stood there straining her eyes for one last glimpse of the Russian eagle fluttering from the disappearing masthead.

The year passed, and another may burst into bloom, but Rezanof did not come. Concepción waited.

Another torturing year went by, and another, and yet others. But Rezanof's flag was seen no more in San Francisco Bay.

California was isolated from the rest of the world, and Concepción could get no news of her lover. But she waited and still waited.

She was besieged by other suitors, one of them a yankee. When Concepción's father was appointed governor of Lower California, she went with him in order to escape their importunities.

At last she gave up all hope of her lover's return. After four years spent with her father in Lower California, she wandered about restlessly, going from place to place, but returning again and again to San Francisco in the hope of learning something about Rezanof.[47]

In this manner she spent 23 years – a barren, cheerless 23 years devoted to caring for the sick and to other charitable work.

Then she joined a religious order but there were then no convents in California, and Concepción, desiring to remain near the scenes of her girlhood, made her

---

[47] Both Concepción's father and her brother served as governor of California during these years, and one may wonder why they made no inquiries regarding Rezanof of visiting Russian ships, seven of which called at San Francisco during the brother's term of office. Castilian pride probably intervened; in addition the younger Arguello was bitterly hostile toward the Russians, presumably because of Rezanof's supposed disloyalty to Concepción.

home with the De La Guerra family at Santa Barbara where she continued her work as a sister of mercy. When, later, the first convent for women was erected in California at Benicia, Concepción entered it, taking the name of Sister Maria Dominica.

But she never ceased to inquire of chance visitors from the world outside for news of Rezanof. She had long since abandoned all hope of ever seeing him again, but she was hungry just to hear his name mentioned. Whenever foreign guests were entertained at Santa Barbara, Concepción was sure to be unobtrusively present in some corner, listening – listening – forever listening. Eventually, Concepción felt, some one of these rovers of the seas would let fall some remark, some bit of vital information – vital to her, at least – that would still the demons of unrest that beleaguered her soul.

Thirty-six years had passed since Concepción had kissed her blonde viking goodbye and bid him godspeed, when in 1842 the English explorer, Sir George Simpson, visited California and in the course of his calls dropped his anchor at Santa Barbara. Sir George, then an elderly man, had explored western North America between California and Alaska and had frequently visited the Russian settlements in Alaska, many years before.

He was hospitably received at Santa Barbara, and a public banquet to which, according to custom, everyone was welcome was given in his honor. There the affairs of the outside world were the subject of animated conversation until a late hour of the night.

Finally one of the guests asked about Rezanof.

"Rezanof? The Count Nikolai Rezanof?" inquired Sir George. "Yes, I knew him quite well."

Instantly silence fell upon the assemblage for in a corner of the hall sat the figure of a dominican sister. The master of ceremonies quickly changed the subject and inquired about other former visitors, and the tension gradually relaxed.

When the feast was ended and the guests were departing, the sister approached Sir George at a moment when he was alone.

"Señor," she said, addressing him, "you said you knew the Count Rezanof. Is he – did he leave Alaska?"

"Yes, Sister, he left Alaska in the year 1806, in the month of august, I believe, never to return."

"Do you know what – what happened – what became of him?"

"I do. He fell sick, shortly after entering Siberia, and was compelled to stop at a Yakut hut. He started on again while still sick, but by the time he reached Yakutsk he was unable to sit on his horse. He remained there, quite ill, for several days, but foolishly resumed his journey while still in a high fever, and collapsed at Krasnoyarsk where he died. He was buried there, and his escort continued on to Saint Petersburg."

Sister Maria had turned her face aside, and Sir George did not observe that her hands were tightly clenched. He went on:

"I understand that Rezanof left a sweetheart in San Francisco. She married, I suppose," he continued musingly, "when Rezanof failed to return."

"No, Señor," replied the sister in a choking voice, "no – she died – too!"

Whether Rezanof really intended to return, or whether he was only using Concepción as a pawn in his game to checkmate Governor Arrillaga and secure the needed supplies never will be known. He died, and so his fidelity was not tested. After examining all the available evidence, the present writers prefer to believe that he intended to return. He was a Russian noble, but Concepción also was of an ancient and honorable family of the Spanish aristocracy, and surely she could not have been over matched by any of the beauties of Saint Petersburg. Then Rezanof's haste in starting home, when his post was in Alaska looking after his colony there, shows that up to the time of his death he was carrying out the course he told Concepción he would pursue.[48]

In 1857 at the convent of Saint Catherine at Benicia, Concepción Arguello died. Professor Chapman gives her this epitaph: "Her life had been famous not only for its romance, but for its kindliness and charities, so that she was loved and venerated by all. So passed away the most cherished figure in the romance of California Alta history."

In the old cemetery of the convent at Benicia, Concepción sleeps beneath a plain cross of brown stone, on which are the words:

SISTER MARIA DOMINICA

O. S. D.

---

[48] It seems to have been Rezanof's intention to turn his intended marriage to the political advantage of Russia by forming an alliance with Spain for the control of the Pacific coast of North America, and he had purposed returning to California via Madrid in order to present his proposal to the king of Spain. If events had gone as he had planned, it is possible that England would have been shut off from the Pacific.

Other Southwestern Legends

Other Southwestern Legends

In addition to the legends that properly belong to one or another of the four southwestern states, there are a few that are not so localized. Of these, three are presented.

The story of Maria Coronel de Agreda is conceded by historians to be the outstanding classic of southwestern lore. It has been the source of a large number of little legends of the Blue Lady, a volume of which could be collected in Texas alone. This is a task awaiting some future Lummis or Robinson.

The myth of the *gran quivira* also has inspired countless treasure legends in Texas and New Mexico. A volume of these already has been published and new ones appear yearly.

The legend of Our Lady of Guadalupe really belongs to Mexico, but it is a part of the lore of the Spanish-americans of our southwest and is so frequently referred to, but not related, by other writers that we here give it in full.

To this group of miscellaneous legends perhaps should be assigned those borrowed from Mexico and Spain. There are several such, believed by people of the southwest to be indigenous but which really were known in Spain or Mexico before there was a Spanish settlement within our borders. One that was told in Spain at least five centuries ago we found in seven widely separated localities from Texas to California.

Our Lady of Guadalupe

On december 9, 1531, a poor indian neophyte named Juan Diego was hurrying over Tepeyac hill, to hear mass in Mexico City.

As he went along the winding path, he pondered over the religious teachings which Bishop Zumarraga and others had instilled into his primitive mind. If Juan understood correctly, beyond the blue firmament there was a home where good Indians might forever have food and shelter without arduous labor. The bishop had assured him of this and had read to him the written words, given by the good God, to prove that this was so.

But, the bishop had explained to him, only a life of service and labor on this earth would open the doors of the other home to him after death. The bishop also had declared many times that Indians must attend mass faithfully if they would keep the favor of the good God.

So, while his neighbors spent their time in idleness or in the hunt, Juan and his family worked in his little corn and bean fields, sharing their meager supplies with the needy and improvident ones about them and consoling themselves with the belief that in the next world their lives would be blessed with plenty and an absence of hardships.

For three years now Juan had been storing up for himself riches in heaven. He had been laboring faithfully with his crops during the week and today, as he stumbled along the path that he had traversed so many times in going to and from mass, he was weary. He found himself wishing that he might lie down among the wild roses that covered the hillside and fall asleep to wake in that other more generous world.

But, no! The bishop had taught him that one must be grateful for the strength to labor and for the opportunity to serve.

Juan shook his head resignedly. Some of these teachings were inexplicable to him, but the bishop must be right. Therefore, he would do his best to obey the teachings faithfully even though he could not entirely understand the necessity.

Juan often had seen pictures and statues of the Holy Mother of Christ in the church or carried at the head of the religious processions. On days like this one, when he was given to meditation, he tried to form a mental image of the living Santissima Maria. The bishop had told him that the Holy Mother loved the Indians the same as she did the white people and that he should address his prayers to her. But Juan never had been able to pray to her directly. She was fair and beautiful as the morning, and gentle as the roses that bloomed along the way. He felt that it would be a sacrilege for one of his humble station to address one so high and so holy. Sometimes, though, he whispered her name reverently. This in itself was a fervent prayer, although he did not realize it.

"Santa Maria! Santissima Maria!" Juan whispered softly, hurrying on as he heard the church chimes in the distance.

"Santissima Maria!"

Suddenly, he felt himself enveloped in a warm radiance that swept over him. He stopped short, startled, looked up; then, without a sound, sank to his knees in the path.

Just ahead of him, surrounded by a pearly glory of light, stood the Mother of Christ!

"Santissima Maria! Santissima Maria!" whispered the Indian, trembling with amazement, his eyes raised in an ecstasy of adoration.

The apparition spoke in tones that seemed to Juan the sweetest music he ever had heard:

"Juan, faithful one! I select you for my messenger to the servant of God, Bishop Zumarraga. Go to him and tell him it is my will that he raise a church to me on this hill, to be a shrine for your people as long as time shall last."

With a smile that seemed a glorious benediction, the Holy Mother vanished.

Juan never knew how he finished his trip to Mexico City, or what time passed before he found himself in the presence of the bishop and other priests. For a while the Indian's words were a mere babbling, so overcome was he with excitement.

His story left the bishop and others staring at him gravely, and with entire skepticism.

"What sign have you, Juan Diego," asked the bishop sternly, "that the Holy Mother of Christ appeared to you?"

The brown man could only stammer that he had no proof, but he insisted that his story was true and that he had faithfully delivered the message that had been entrusted to him by the most Holy Mary.

"The fellow is drunk," commented one of the priests.

So Juan was dismissed ignominiously from the presence of the churchmen and warned that a repetition of such conduct would result in severe punishment for blasphemy.

Juan departed, bewildered, wondering if, after all, he had but dreamed. In that state he made his way back to the top of Tepeyac hill. There in the sandy soil were the imprints of his knees, where he had knelt before the Virgin Mary. He knew now that he had not dreamed. The memory of the vision rose vividly before him, and instinctively he sank again to his knees in the same spot, breathing worshipfully,

"Santissima Maria! Santissima Maria!"

Hardly had the whisper left his lips when, with a rush of warm, silent light, the Holy Mother again stood before him!

"Gather your cloak full of these roses, Juan," she instructed him, "and take them to the bishop. He shall have the sign he requires. Fear nothing."

The apparition vanished. Juan sprang to his feet. His hand trembled as he rapidly broke the wild roses from their stems. His mind bewildered, nevertheless was filled with a conviction that the Holy Mother had a purpose in her instruction. All the weariness left his body. Peace and happiness surged through him, wiping out the darkness and misery that had oppressed his primitive soul. For he, a humble Indian, had twice seen the Santissima Maria! She had addressed him!

For the second time that morning Juan Diego stood before the bishop. He no longer was trembling; his eyes shone with the light of an awakened soul; he stood proudly erect. He was the messenger of the Holy Mother of God!

He opened his cloak and, as the mass of roses tumbled to the floor, a sharp reproof rose to the tongue of the bishop. If the Indian wished to offer flowers to the church, he should have arranged them tastefully and presented them to the altar. But before the bishop could speak, his eyes fell upon Juan's cloak. He slowly rose to his feet, utter amazement written on his face. For there, on the coarsely-woven fabric, was imprinted a clear, beautiful, life-size likeness of the Holy Mother!

The church was built on Tepeyac hill on the spot where the Virgin Mary had appeared to Juan Diego, and was dedicated to *Nuestra Senora de Guadalupe* (Our Lady of Guadalupe).

It has become a famous shrine for catholic pilgrims, hundreds of thousands of whom visit it yearly. Its interior is crowded with votive offerings of every sort, humble and costly. Outside the church are the famous sails of Guadalupe – a representation in stone of the sails of a ship, erected by some sailors as a token of their gratitude for rescue from shipwreck by Our Lady of Guadalupe, who is the patron saint of the Mexicans both in Mexico and the United States.

Within the church is to be seen the cloak of Juan Diego with its image of the Virgin Mary, zealously guarded as one of the priceless relics of christendom. The story of that cloak is known to every Mexican in America.

One version of this legend declares that the roses which Juan Diego gathered had miraculously burst into bloom with the appearance of the Virgin Mary, and pictures of her as Our Lady of Guadalupe always have a festooned border of roses.

The events of the legend took place in december, but in the latitude of Mexico City roses bloom all year.

Maria Coronel

One of the most remarkable things about the story of Maria Coronel de Agreda is the fact that it is not widely known. As a mystery, this woman ranks above any of the shadowy, baffling characters who have flitted across the pages of history to the mystification of following generations.

The life of Maria Coronel is well known. She was born in Agreda, Spain, in 1602 and died there in 1665. She was one of the prominent women of her time. She was very devout, and in 1619 at the age of seventeen she joined a religious order, spending the rest of her life in a large institution that had been founded by her parents at Agreda for the care and education of the poor.

In 1629, when she was but 27 years old, the pope made her the head of both her order and the institution. Maria retained that position until her death. Under her management the school came to have a wide-spread reputation. Maria also was a writer, being the author of several books on religious subjects. Some of these are still in existence, as well as many of her manuscripts.

As a young woman Maria was beautiful. She lived in an atmosphere of altruism and idealism. The christianizing of the Indians of the New World always was prominent in her thoughts, and it is certain that this devotion to the Indians colored her entire life.

Now Maria claimed to have made numerous visits

to the Indians of New Spain, principally to those of Texas but also to those of New Mexico, Arizona, and Mexico. She wrote accounts of her visits, describing the Indians, their habitations, etc., and even giving the tribal names in some instances. Some of these were tribes that already had been seen by Spanish explorers, but no white person other than Maria Coronel saw certain other tribes until 24 years after her death. It is said she described these in some detail and that here, as elsewhere, her descriptions were later found to be correct. The present writers have seen no copies of those descriptions.

Her last visit to the New World, according to her own statement, was made in 1631, when she was 29 years of age.

Evidence that she actually had been among the Indians was found by the first white men to visit them; this is fully authenticated. Fray Alonso de Benavides, who was custodian of the New Mexico mission field from 1625 to 1630, was visited at that time (presumably in 1626) by a delegation of Indians from east of the Manzaño mountains, who had come posthaste to him to ask that missions be established in their territory. Benavides wrote:

We asked them why they petitioned us for baptism with so much fervor, and for missionaries to instruct them. They replied that a woman, like the woman of whom we had a picture – it was a picture of Madre Luisa de Carion – had come to preach to them in their own tongue, ordering them to go and summon the padres to instruct and baptize them, and that they should lose no time in doing this. Moreover (they said) the woman who had preached to them was dressed precisely as was the woman of our picture, but that her features were different and that she was young and beautiful. And after this, when other Indians came from the same tribes and looked at our picture, they all agreed that the clothing was the same but that the face was not the same; that the face of the woman who had come to preach to them was that of a young, beautiful girl.[49]

In 1689 De Leon, who led the expedition in search of La Salle's fort near Matagorda Bay, wrote of the Indians of that region:

They perform many christian rites, and the indian governor asked us for missionaries to instruct them, saying that many years ago a woman went inland to instruct them, but that she had not been there for a long time.

In the following year Fray Damian Manzanet visited the Indians of eastern Texas, and in his report we find the following:

While we were at the Tejas village, after we had distributed clothing to the Indians and to the chief of the Tejas, this chief asked me for a piece of blue baize to make a shroud for his mother when she died; I told him that cloth would be more suitable and he answered that he wanted no color but blue. I then asked him what mysterious reason he had for preferring the blue color, and in reply he said they were very fond of that color, particularly for burial clothes, because in times past they had been visited frequently by a very beautiful woman, who came down from the hills dressed in blue garments, and that they wished to do as that woman had done. On my asking whether that had been long since, the chief said it was before his time, but his mother, who was very old, had seen that woman, as also had other old people. From this it is easily to be seen that they referred to the Madre Maria de Jesus de Coronel, as she herself acknowledged to the father custodian of New Mexico, her last visit having been made in 1631, this last fact being evident from her own statement to the said father custodian.[50]

---

[49] Maria Coronel and Luisa de Carion belonged to the same religious order, hence the similarity of garb. The fact that the Indians identified the dress of their mysterious visitor is evidence that they also clearly remembered her features.

[50] The father custodian here referred to was Fray Alonso de Benavides.

Still another reference to this woman is found in another of Manzanet's letters, written also in 1690:

The blessed Madre Maria tells of having been frequently in New Mexico and to the *gran quivira,* adding that eastward from the *gran quivira* are the tribes of the Ticlas, Theas, and Caburcols.

Next we have the following episode occurring at the San Augustine mission in western Texas, date not known but it was after the year 1668, in which year that mission was founded:

A band of five Indians from beyond the Pecos river arrived one morning, saying they had been sent by their tribe to ask for a priest to come and live with them. They informed the padres of that mission that "A woman strangely dressed had visited their people many years before, and had made known to them the life and doctrines of Jesus Christ; that her visits to them had been many, and that it was she who had told them to come to the missionaries. Where she lived, and how she had come, they did not know."

Finally reference is found to this mysterious young woman in letters written between 1710 and 1714 by the Frenchman, Saint-Denis, who was frequently in eastern Texas during that period. He wrote that the Indians of those regions called for blue cloth in which to bury their dead, saying that a woman dressed in blue had come to them a great many years before and had baptized, among others, the medicine man of their village, and they wanted their dead to be like that woman in the next world.

As to Maria's presence in Arizona, there is only one recorded item of evidence. Padre Eusebio Kino stated in his journal that during his journey to the Gila river

in 1690 the Indians of that region told him of a group
of white men, who many years before had passed down
the Gila river to the head of the Gulf of California and
back, and of a woman dressed in blue, who some years
later had visited them and preached to them in an
unknown tongue, and who twice had risen from the
dead after having been shot with arrows by the Indians
of the Colorado river region.

Now the story that the natives told Kino of the
white men was a true account of Oñate's journey to
the Gulf of California in 1605, although 85 years had
elapsed since that journey was made. There can be
no doubt, therefore, that they also handed down what
appeared to them to be the facts in the case of the
woman in blue.

In 1773 Fray Junipero Serra of California mentioned Maria Coronel in a letter to Fray Palou. This
mention is accepted by some writers as evidence that
Maria had visited that region, but the present writers
cannot accept it as such. Serra merely stated that it
appeared Maria's prophecy regarding the conversion
of the Indians of that region was about to be fulfilled.
It was not necessary for her to leave Spain in order
to make such a prophecy.

As to the legendary evidence today of her presence
on this side of the ocean, Robert Sturmberg of Texas
sums it up thus:

From the swamps of western Louisiana and eastern Texas, throughout Texas, Mexico, New Mexico, Arizona, and California, her
memory lives and will live forever in the folklore and traditions of
those people whose Indian ancestors were blessed with the visits of
this saintly woman. Among the Tezcucan and other Indian tribes of
Texas and Mexico, she is known as the Mysterious Woman in Blue,

for the blue color of her habit seems to have been specially impressed upon the memory of these primitive children of nature.

Opposed to all this conclusive evidence of Maria's actual presence among the Indians of our southwest, there is also conclusive evidence that she never once set foot out of Spain and that very probably she never once was absent from Agreda after she was seventeen years old.

Regarding her own statements of her visits to the Indians, in 1631 she made written confession that those visits were made only in trances. The original of that document has not been found and for this reason it has been charged that copies of it are forgeries. However, Bancroft apparently accepted it as genuine. Whether true or not, Maria made oral confession to the same effect to Fray Benavides, as he himself recorded. It is significant that she made no more visits after the year 1631. She informed Benavides that she sometimes made several visits in the course of one day, and she related to him one incident that had occurred in his presence in New Mexico wherein she also was present but invisible to him.

Writers who maintain that Maria was in the New World in person fail to cite any evidence from Spanish sources that she ever was out of Spain, or even absent from the institution at Agreda of which she was the head. In her time a detailed *auto* was made of every little event, however trivial, and Maria could not have absented herself for even one day without the fact being minutely recorded, together with a record of her return and the reasons for her absence. Yet it would have taken her about one year, under favorable circumstances, to make a round trip from Agreda to New Mexico or Texas and back.

Moreover, in those days a woman was not permitted to depart alone for America. No one could embark without the permission of the authorities, and a record was made of every one taking ship. To have gone as a stowaway was impossible, and the unexplained absence of a person as prominent as was Maria Coronel would have resulted in a farflung search for her.

Assuming that she could have left Spain without the fact being permanently recorded, she could have landed nowhere in North America except at Vera Cruz. Between Vera Cruz and eastern Texas lie 1100 miles of mountainous country, crossed by six unfordable rivers, while between that port and New Mexico lies an equal expanse of desert country wherein sources of drinking water are sometimes four days' journey, on foot, apart.

Yet, according to the testimony of the Indians and later indian traditions, this young woman always traveled alone, on foot, without provisions, baggage, or impedimenta of any kind, and they never knew whence she came or whither she went. No tradition speaks of her as asking or receiving either food or water. One legend says she refused food.

There are two points that, so far as our reading has gone, have been overlooked by other writers. One is that Maria avoided contact with others of her race in America. We find not a trace of evidence that she ever was seen by anyone, except Indians, on this side of the Atlantic. It is difficult to understand how she escaped detection for, whatever direction she traveled from Vera Cruz, her route for some distance would have lain through Spanish settlements.

The other point is that, except in Arizona, she appears to have talked to the Indians in their own tongues. In New Mexico, Indians who had seen her only a short time before told Benavides that she preached to them in their own tongue, and the different tribes of Texas apparently had no difficulty in understanding her exposition of christian doctrines.

A final question may arise in the reader's mind. If it were impossible for Maria to leave Spain without the fact being prominently recorded, why did Fray Benavides and Fray Manzanet accept her presence here as something not to be doubted?

In the first place, it appears that Benavides did doubt for upon his return to Spain he interviewed Maria and, apparently, subjected her to a searching interrogatory, whereupon her confession followed. Also, the mind of those days was extremely credulous; people from the highest to the lowest believed in the supernatural and miraculous to an extent quite inconceivable in these modern times. Even Benavides, educated and practical, accepted Maria's explanation of her visits to the Indians. The fact that a phenomenon was subversive of natural laws was no argument whatever against its reality.

Most students of the life of Maria Coronel refrain from recording any opinions of their own, and we follow their example. Other writers have taken one or another of the following views:

That Maria Coronel actually visited widely separated indian tribes in person; that her visits were made in trances, as she confessed; that the Indians were visited by some young, female missionary, whose identity is unknown, and that Maria assumed the identity of this woman.

We quote without comment the conclusions of a leading exponent of each theory.

Robert Sturmberg,[51] after citing the testimony of the Indians that we already have presented, states that

Against all this evidence of Maria's personal presence among the various indian tribes and in the missions, there exists only a copy of what is said to be a statement of the venerable (sic) madre, dated may 15, 1631, in which she is alleged to have confessed that these visits were only apparitions. . . Moreover, it does hardly stand to reason that Fray Damian, in the year 1690, should not have known of this statement, should it really have existence. . . The conclusion, therefore, seems justified that Madre Maria de Jesus de Agreda really visited the western hemisphere.

Later in his argument, however, Mr. Sturmberg apparently becomes noncommittal:

. . . quite a controversy is being carried on today (1921) about her visits to the indian tribes. Till date the matter has neither been settled officially nor explained satisfactorily. Catholic historians, generally, seem to prefer the view that her case "appears to be an established case of clairvoyant trance."

Adina de Zavala[52] takes the view that Maria never left Spain:

The strange part of the story is that Mary de Agreda had never really been in Texas or the New World in person; but during her state of intense longing and continued prayer, she must have dreamed all, or visited them (the Indians) in ecstasy — but so vivid were those dreams, if dreams they were, and so many times were they repeated and the same country and people held in vision before her mind day

---

[51] In *History of San Antonio and the early days in Texas,* 37.
[52] Zavala, *History and legends of the Alamo,* 105-106.

after day and month after month, that they became as real to her as those among whom she actually lived. . . Stranger yet is the fact that the people of these tribes saw her, loved and remembered her, and that she seemed real to them.

Charles H. Heimsath [53] states that

After the publication of his *Memoria* in 1630, Benavides visited Maria de Jesus de Agreda. She was already famous because of the publication of her *La Mistica de Dios Historia Divina de la Virgin, Madre de Dios,* in 1627. . . The mind of this woman . . . was fertile for the story of Benavides. She immediately assumed the identity of the unknown female missionary; and, in the course of the visit, which lasted probably two weeks, elaborated fully the exact method of the holy visitations. Benavides, with his charming medieval mind, readily accepted her story. Because of the prominence of the two . . . it obtained rapid and wide circulation and credence.

Many writers have touched briefly upon some aspect of the story of Maria Coronel, or Maria de Jesus de Agreda as she was known in her religious order. However, so far as we can learn, no one writer to date has presented all the facts that we have assembled. We offer nothing new; our work is merely a compilation of what others have recorded.[54]

[53] Dobie, *Legends of Texas,* 132.

[54] In the preparation thereof we have consulted the following sources, each of which has contributed something to the foregoing narrative: Bolton, *Southwestern historical quarterly,* XVI, no. 1; Schmitt, *Texas state historical quarterly,* I; Heimsath, "Legends of the blue lady" in *Legends of Texas,* compiled by Dobie; Sturmberg, *History of San Antonio and the early days in Texas;* Zavala, *History and legends of the Alamo;* Harris, *Occultism, spiritism and demonology;* Shea, *The catholic church in colonial days;* Buckingham Smith, *Documentos para la historia de la Florida;* and Hodge, *Bibliography of Fray Alonso de Benavides,* III. Manzanet's testimony is found, in translation, in the *Texas state historical quarterly,* II; and of Benavides in *The memorial of Fray Alonso de Benavides,* translated by Mrs. Edward E. Ayer.

Legends of the Blue Lady

Many little stories of the Blue Lady, or the Lady in Blue, are to be found in the San Antonio valley of Texas, and especially in and around San Antonio among the people of part indian blood.

In the vicinity of that city, it is said there are remains of old subterranean passages, so nearly obliterated that their courses can now no longer be traced. It is supposed by many that these tunnels connected the different missions, but more probably they were subterranean outlets through which the people of the missions could escape unseen when hard pressed by hostile Indians.

The Mexicans of San Antonio say that one of these underground passages – no person knows, or can know, which one – leads to an enchanted city under the earth, inhabited by mysterious people, who occasionally appear among mankind on missions of benevolence, charity, or mercy. The two principal characters inhabiting this city under the ground are the Padre and the Blue Lady.

The stories of the Padre are simple little tales reciting his numerous acts of charity toward the living. This legendary character clearly is none other than Padre Antonio Margil, the saintly old priest who founded the first mission in San Antonio.

More prominent than the Padre, in the lore of the Mexicans, is the Blue Lady. She lives in a wonderful palace under the ground, from which she frequently comes forth to bless and comfort the afflicted. Usually, but not always, children are the recipients of her favors. To one woman in each generation the Blue Lady appears and upon her confers some priceless mental or spiritual endowment, whereby that woman stands above and apart from other women. In a sense the Blue Lady is not a legendary character for she still lives, say the Mexican story-tellers, and has lived for four centuries.

Incidentally, the stories of the Blue Lady are not told to every passerby. A stranger will hear none of them from the lips of the Mexicans. Unless one has won the confidence and esteem of those people and is welcome at their firesides, they will not open their mouths and they regard with suspicion, perhaps not unjustified, the Anglo-american who too obviously attempts to make their acquaintances.

Only one of the many Texas legends of the Blue Lady is presented. It is a typical one that has been told for one and one-half centuries.

In the early days of Texas the present site of San Antonio was occupied by three distinct villages: San Antonio de Bexar, San Fernando, and the indian community of San Antonio de Valero. From 1780 to about 1800 the Valero community with its large buildings, walled courtyards, and rows of indian cabins was deserted. It was within this period that the events of our story took place.

In San Fernando lived José Valdez with his wife and their child, Ursula. José who had been wounded in one of the numerous battles with the Comanches, was unable to work. There were surgeons in Mexico City who could have restored him to health and activity, but he was without money. His wife, compelled to do menial work in order to support the home, was able to provide only the barest necessities for the three of them.

One day Ursula, a girl of seven years, went with her playmates to gather flowers in the chapel courtyard of the Valero, flowers having taken possession of the convento garden after the mission was abandoned.

When the time passed for Ursula to have reached home, and she did not appear, the mother started out to look for her. She visited the courtyards of the Valero, but the children had all gone, and her calling brought no answer.

She became alarmed, for the Comanches frequently lurked about, unseen, watching for an opportunity to steal children or horses. She ran to the homes of some of Ursula's playmates, but they remembered only that Ursula had separated from them while they were playing games, whereupon they assumed that she had gone home.

The mother now was frantic, and she aroused the men of the community to aid in the search, telling them not to alarm her husband, who was ill and helpless.

The men searched around the Valero for indian tracks, but found nothing. Night fell, and the searchers obtained lanterns and continued their hunt. They were about to give it up, when one of them happened to think of a tiny room hidden in the base of the farthest tower of the old convento. There he found the child, curled up in a corner, asleep. He woke her, and soon she was restored to her mother.

Ursula now explained to her mother that they had

been playing, and she had hidden from all the rest, when a lady dressed in blue, who for some reason had entered the old courtyard, caught her dress on a bush and fell, wrenching her ankle. The little girl ran to the woman, disentangled her dress, helped her to her feet, and aided her as she limped out through the gate near which Ursula had been hiding. In return for this assistance the lady gave Ursula a small but heavy packet, which the child dropped into the pocket of her apron. Then the woman, apparently completely recovered, walked briskly away, and Ursula, observing that the other children had not seen her, darted back into her hiding place and curled up in a dark corner. She knew no more until she was awakened by a man with a lantern standing beside her, exclaiming, *"Sacramento! Diablita!* To cause us so much worry! Come you with me to your mother, quickly!"

Then she fished the packet out of her pocket and gave it to her mother. Curious to know what it contained, the woman unwrapped it, and then ran to her husband screaming for joy. The packet contained gold money and a number of pearls and diamonds!

So here were found the means to send José to the surgeons in Mexico City. His health was restored, and he again was able to work at his trade and support his family; and peace and happiness again reigned in the little home that so lately had been enveloped in despair.

Unquestionably the child had encountered the Blue Lady, for no such woman as she described lived in the community, nor did any woman there own such gems as had been given to Ursula. The Blue Lady had only pretended to be injured, in order to test Ursula's kindness of heart.

A few stories of the Blue Lady are to be found in New Mexico, but whether they are indigenous or have been imported from Texas is not known. We recite a typical one, but we can reproduce only the general sense of the narrator's words.

"Yes, the Blue Lady used to visit our people in the years long gone. But now she does not often come, and when she does she does not enter our village. Yet she brings only good with her.

"Blue flowers spring up wherever her feet touch the ground. She loves the daytime, and does not appear at night. When the sky has a wonderful deep color of blue, when there is a more joyful note to the songs of birds, whenever there is a fresher greenness on the grass, we know, even though we do not see her, that the Blue Lady is near.

"Oh, yes, Señor, we have seen her. I have seen her. But she never approaches our dwellings. She never is close enough that her face might be seen, but she can be known by the blue of her clothing and by the gladness that nature puts on when she is near.

"Pursue or approach her, Señor? *Que sacrilegio!* Why molest her who brings only blessings with her? Is it not clear that because of her never approaching us, she wishes never to be approached? If we tried to come near her, she would vanish from our sight and would no more visit our country.

"Yet, Señor, there was a time in the days long gone, but not yet so long gone as the days when she visited our far-off ancestors, when the Blue Lady was seen to move and when she did permit one to approach her. It was in this manner, Señor, with your permission.

"The young war-chief of our pueblo had gone to the mountains, far away to the south, with a party, in a hunt for deer and bear.

"While they were engaged in hunting and killing the deer and bear, there came a runner from that chief's village, with the word that the chief's wife was stricken with sickness, and that he should return home at once.

"This runner stayed with the hunters and the chief departed without delay, and, wishing to reach his pueblo as soon as possible, he struck out across that part of the country known to the white men as *la jornada del muerte,* where there is no water to be found for two days of traveling.

"He journeyed by the north star, but the night became clouded and he lost his way, for he followed no trail, and he wandered about that night and the next day and far into the next night, seeking water.

"By this time he was exceedingly tired and sore of foot, and was in such state that he was prepared to die. Then he saw before him the Blue Lady, beckoning him on. He stumbled along after her, and after a while she stopped. When he came up he saw, beside her, a spring of fresh water, and he fell on his breast and drank his fill. When he rose to give thanks to the Blue Lady, she was not anywhere. But even as he drank the north star broke through the clouds, whereby he guided his footsteps on through *la jornada del muerte* and to his own village where, at sight of him, his wife began to get well.

"And the spring is there today, Señor; the only water to drink that is to be found in the whole country of *la jornada del muerte."*

The legends of the Blue Lady become fewer west-ward from Texas. None could be found in California, although Sturmberg states that "In . . . California, the trace of Madre Maria is found in numerous legends and beautiful folklore."

The following one was gleaned in southern Arizona.

"Si, la Señorita Azul (the Blue Lady) visited this country in times now afar off. Before the grandfather of my grandmother's grandfather lived. The story is even as I shall tell it.

"It was, as I have said, so many years ago that no man can count them. The chief of the Papago people was very old. He loved the son of his son, who one day himself would be a chief; and he loved the boy the more for the reason that the boy's father, who was the old chief's son, was dead.

"But this boy now lay very sick in the lodge of his mother, and for two days the people of the village had made prayers to their gods to spare the boy's life. But these prayers did not help, nor was the magic of the medicine men of any avail.

"It was as I have said when, at the end of a day, the men and women of the village, having partaken of their evening meal, were sitting about their fire in the plaza, but the children all were in the lodges and asleep. All were silent and were heavy of spirit be-cause of the sickness that lay upon the son of the chief's son.

"Now, while they were so, there came a flash of white light so bright that every one was blinded by it, and when sight came slowly back to their eyes, they saw standing before them a young woman, clothed in strange robes of blue, and, my brother, she was of a beauty like to that of the full moon rising over quiet waters.

"All were filled with fear and were unable to say or move. Then the young woman spoke to them, and bade them have no fear, but to listen to her words.

"Thereupon she told them of a new god, whereof they had not known before, and who was not like to any of their gods, but chief of them all. For a long time she spoke, and her tongue was like to the music of a mountain stream to the ears of a very thirsty man.

"Then, to make known to them that she was sent by the god whereof she had told them, she asked if there were any sick in their village, and when she asked this she looked at the old chief.

"Thereupon he sprang to his feet, and said that the son of his son was sick and near to death.

"He told her, 'We have prayed to our gods, and they have done nothing. If now your god can restore him that is sick, we will know that he is the ruler of all gods.'

"So *la Señorita Azul* asked that she be led to where the sick boy lay, and the old chief led the way.

"When they reached the lodge wherein the sick boy lay, she placed her hand on his forehead and began saying prayers to the god whereof she had spoken. The boy's mother was filled with fear at this, and would have prevented it, but she was restrained by the old chief who bade her be quiet.

"*La Señorita Azul* so prayed and held her hand on the boy's head for the time it would take to smoke a small pipe, the while the people stood about outside the lodge in wonder.

"When she took away her hand, the boy's eyes opened, and he smiled, and his distemper was gone, and he asked that food be given him. But *la Señorita Azul* forbade, saying, 'Give him water, but give him no food until the morrow.'

"Then the people were all filled with joy, and made much noise, and they followed *la Señorita Azul* from the lodge and begged her to remain with them, and asked her what food she desired.

"But she denied them, and answered that she must not stay and must not eat of any food. But in time to come, she told them, teachers would appear, to tell them how to live after the manner of her people, and to tell them more of the chief of all gods of whom she had spoken.

"Then a sleepiness came over all, so that they knew nothing, and when they woke the woman was gone, although the red of the sunset, which still sat upon the mountain tops, made clear to them that they had slept for but a moment. They thought that they all had but dreamed, but when they hastened to the lodge wherein the son of the chief's son lay, they found him sleeping, and his mother, who had stayed with him, made assurance that all had happened as had appeared to happen.

"No, Señor, she came no more; or, if she did, the tale of her coming has not been passed down to us. But the teachers came, as she had foretold, and they told our people about the god of the white men, and how to live even as the white people lived."

The authors sought diligently for the legend of the Blue Lady that was mentioned by Kino in his journal of 1690. If found, it would have been the only existing legend of Maria Coronel that has come down from her own day exclusively through the Indians. But apparently it no longer exists. The tribe from which Kino obtained the story can not be identified; probably it is now extinct.

It may interest the reader to learn that, according to Mr. Will Robinson, a journalist of New Mexico, the Navajo Indians in 1935 and 1936 were excited over a predicted return of the Blue Lady. They refused to divulge the source of their information, but declared with complete assurance that a visit by the Blue Lady was impending. Whether they still await her, we do not know.

The Gran Quivira

Europe, at the time of the discovery of America, was hardly emerged from the intellectual mists of the dark ages. The world still was ruled by superstition. Four centuries ago, before man's imagination had become shackled by exploration and scientific research, there was no limit to human credulity.

For that reason, the discovery of new continents beyond the western ocean probably was a more remarkable thing to the people of that time than would be, to us, the arrival within our reach of a new planet. To Europe, the Americas were not the other half of a rather commonplace world; they comprised a new world – a world of mysteries, wonders, and enchantments.

Ponce de Leon, seeking a fountain of youth, was not the fool he often is pictured as being. He was as rational as any man and more intelligent and capable than were most of his contemporaries, as is proved by his own record as a military man and executive. He had the courage and enterprise to seek the thing that other men were sure existed somewhere in the Americas.

Returned voyagers, who really had seen nothing marvelous in the New World, nevertheless told amazing stories of what they had heard from the natives, and it is probable that the Indians, observing the credulity of the newcomers, obliged them to the limit of the indian imagination.

Thus voyagers heard of cities and even of mountain ranges of pure gold; they heard of great rivers flowing over measureless golden sands; they heard of reefs of pearls; they were told of fountains of youth, of springs gushing forth wine of unexcelled bouquet, of islands peopled by Amazonian houris, of fruits that would make the pomegranates of Eden taste like dry husks in comparison.

Most of the extravagant beliefs concerning the New World died out as voyager after voyager returned without any tangible evidence to support such wild fancies; but there were a few that persisted, and the most persistent one was of a native kingdom, or principality, in which gold and precious stones abounded, and where the chief city, or cities, were lavishly adorned with gold and silver.

This myth, with its variants, was pursued in vain over two continents by Spaniards, Englishmen, Frenchmen, Portuguese, and even by the Dutch and Germans. History preserves the names of but a few of those who adventured for the grand treasure. Their number was legion, and many of them died seeking the mystic city of gold.

With the legend of "El Dorado" (the gilded man) we have little to do, for the country of El Dorado was sought only in South America. Briefly, this story was of a district so rich in gold that the ruler thereof used gold dust instead of soap in his daily bath.

In North America the tradition of a golden kingdom first took definite form in the myth of the "Seven Cities of Cibola." The origin of this story was as follows:

When in 1527 Nuño de Guzmán was ruling at Pañuco, Mexico, an Indian told him of seven populous villages far to the northwest, wherein there were silversmiths and workers in precious stones. The imaginations of the adventurers of Mexico seized upon this story and magnified it with each telling, until those seven pueblos grew into seven magnificent and fabulously wealthy cities, located somewhere in the unknown land to the north. Guzmán himself started in search of them, but he got no farther than the southern limits of the present Mexican state of Sonora.

Nine years later Cabeza de Vaca also heard of those villages, and when Marcos de Niza was sent northward to investigate, he saw one of the Zuñi group from a distance, the mirage effect of the atmosphere elevating its terraces into lofty towers, and the setting sun transmuting its walls into weathered gold; and he hastened back to Mexico with a wonderful story.[55]

The following year (1540) Coronado demolished the myth of the magnificent Seven Cities of Cibola, when he found them to be only seven impoverished indian pueblos.

The Cibolan myth had lived but thirteen years. But it was reborn immediately in the story of the kingdom of Quivira. During the winter (1540-1541) that Coronado remained encamped at the pueblo of Tiguex on the Rio Grande, a captive Plains Indian of the Cicuyé pueblo told him of a country of vast riches lying far to the east, and this country the Spaniards named Quivira, or the kingdom of Quivira.

[55] The writers have no documentary evidence that the pueblo had any such appearance to Marcos, but in no other way can his gross but unintentional exaggeration be explained. The writers themselves have seen indian pueblos and other structures greatly elevated by atmospheric refraction and gilded by the setting sun, and can, therefore, understand Marcos's error.

The origin of the name is not definitely known. Some writers believe it to be Indian. We have been advised that it was derived from the name by which the Wichita Indians called themselves, but those Indians called themselves *Ki-ti-ki-ti-sh,* which does not sound much like Quivira. Mr. Robert Sturmberg offers an explanation that is not impossible:

Coronado had given his men as a watch-word the shibboleth, "Quien vivira, vera," or "He who lives shall see." His men at once shortened this to "Quien vivira," and then, by one of those progressive mutations with which philologists are familiar, to "Qui'vivira" and then to "Quivira."

Whatever its origin, this term arose in Coronado's army and was applied to the region to which their indian guide was conducting them. The kingdom of Quivira proved to be but a village of straw-thatched lodges in eastern Kansas, but the name remained attached to that district.

When Coronado again reached New Mexico after that long journey into Kansas, the Pueblo Indians told him that his guide had misled him; in fact, one other Indian who had accompanied Coronado had insisted all along that the guide, Turco, was lying, and that the golden Quivira lay to the southeast of Cicuyé. Coronado was laying plans to pursue this new clue when a nearly fatal accident caused him to give up the project and return to Mexico.

Now it is this fabled wealth that Coronado was told of, but did not seek, that is the foundation, or inspiration, for all the stories that have arisen during the last one and one-half century regarding the *gran quivira.*

So far as we can learn, all such legends have been born within the last 150 years. There is no evidence that the Spaniards, after Coronado's time, attached the idea of wealth to that name. To them it was but the name of a rather indefinite district somewhere east of the Rio Grande.

The name later came to mean to the Mexicans and Anglo-americans a "great treasure" and legend has located this treasure, or its source, in the region east of the Manzaño mountains of New Mexico and in the San Saba district of Texas. Both these districts lie southeastward from the Cicuyé pueblo. But there are other reasons why legend has placed the *gran quivira* in one or the other of these two places.

In the former region are remains of large indian pueblos and the ruins of three pretentious missions, all of which were abandoned in the 1670's because of increasing pressure from the Apaches. These ruins, the history of which was not known until late in the nineteenth century, gave rise to the tradition that here was the *gran quivira* that eluded Coronado; that later Spaniards had worked rich mines in that vicinity and had cached the bullion there or elsewhere in New Mexico during the Pueblo rebellion of 1680. The ruined mission buildings have even been identified as smelters, etc. Consequently, for the last one and one-half centuries that region has been ransacked for treasure, and the name *gran quivira* even has been fastened upon the ruins of the old Tabira mission, the real history of which is now well known. Under that name the Tabira mission was made a national monument, and appears so named on the maps of today.

As regards the *gran quivira* of Texas, it has been
pointed out that while the Pueblo Indians of New
Mexico advised Coronado to go southeastward if he
would find the gold he was seeking, the Indians of
Louisiana directed the French to go westward, and
those of Nuevo Leon in Mexico advised the Spaniards
to go northward, in their search for gold and silver.
These three lines would intersect in the San Saba district. Furthermore, there is some evidence that a mine
of some sort was opened in the San Saba country in
1750, and there is a record of 30 mule-loads of ore
having been sent to Mexico City for assay. Nothing
came of this; hence we may conclude that the ore was
not worth reducing, if, in fact, it contained any gold
or silver at all. But unauthenticated tradition states
that there was a very rich mine there, and that the ore
was reduced in the vicinity and the bullion cached.
Those 30 mule-loads of ore have given rise to a great
many treasure legends, in which the ore is converted
to gold or silver amounting, in different legends, to
from 5 to 500 mule-loads.

Bancroft has shown that no mining of any kind was
done in New Mexico prior to 1725 and nothing more
than mere prospecting prior to 1804. Subsequent students have verified his findings. In 1804 a copper mine
was opened in southwestern New Mexico; this marks
the whole extent of mining in this state during the
Spanish period. In fact, there is no evidence that the
Spaniards ever found gold or silver in paying quantities
in our southwestern states, nor did any but the early
conquistadores ever seek wholeheartedly for it. The
colonial Spaniards of New Mexico and Texas had all
they could do to raise their crops of corn, frijoles, and

grapes, and fight off predatory Apaches and Comanches without giving much attention to gold-seeking. Yet every old Spanish building in the southwest, except such as have been continuously occupied or guarded, has been tunneled, pitted, and undermined by searchers for wealth that never existed.

While the matter-of-fact historians and the unimaginative mineralogists of the United States Geological Survey assure us that neither the *gran quivira* of New Mexico nor that of Texas ever had any foundation of fact, yet many people still believe in the existence of one or both, and each year bears its crop of legends of this treasure. As late as the year, 1932, certain individuals were seeking legislative appropriations to enable them to seek anew in the Salinas district of New Mexico the treasure of the *gran quivira*. Even as we are preparing this narrative there comes to our notice, in the press, the latest of the stories of that wealth; this time it is cached somewhere in the San Andreas mountains, about 150 miles from its place of origin in the *gran quivira* region.

So the myth, born of the medieval imagination, lives in twentieth century America and forms the one surviving link that binds us to the adventuring conquistadores of old Spain.

Bibliography

Bibliography

AUSTIN, MARY. The land of journeys' ending (New York, 1924).
A picturesque but somewhat disconnected narrative of the sedentary Indians of the southwest.

BANCROFT, HUBERT HOWE. Works (San Francisco, 1882-1890).
Bancroft's works, now to an extent superseded, still remain a valuable source of reference material. Volumes IX to XXIV deal with Mexico and the southwest.

BENAVIDES, FRAY ALONSO DE. His memorial translated by Mrs. Edward E. Ayer, annotated by F. W. Hodge and C. F. Lummis (Chicago, privately printed, 1916).
An account of New Mexico in 1625-1630.

BIDWELL, GENERAL JOHN. Echoes of the past (New York, 1929).

BLACKMAR, F. W. Spanish institutions of the southwest (Baltimore, 1891).

BOLTON, H. E. Spanish exploration in the southwest, 1542-1706 (New York, 1916).

———— Texas in the middle eighteenth century (Berkeley, 1915).

CASTEÑADA, CARLOS EDUARDO. Silent years in Texas history: in *Southwestern historical quarterly* (Austin) october, 1934.

CASTEÑADA, PEDRO DE. Relacion de la jornada de Cibola, translated by George Parker Winship: published in Bureau of ethnology *Fourteenth annual report*, I.
An account of Coronado's expedition by one of its personnel. A translation of Jaramillo's *Relacion* is found in the same volume.

CHAPMAN, C. E. History of California; Spanish period (New York, 1926).
A good one-volume history of Spanish California.

CHASE, J. S. and C. F. Saunders. The California padres and their missions (New York, 1915).
Contains more reminiscence and legend than history.

DOBIE, J. FRANK. Texas and southwestern lore (Austin, 1927).
Mostly folk-songs of the Mexican and early Anglo-american periods.

———— Legends of Texas (Austin, 1924).

Mostly of the Anglo-american frontier.

———— Coronado's children (Austin, 1931).

A collection of the treasure legends born of the *gran quivira* myth.

DUELL, PRENT. Mission architecture (Tucson, 1919).

A discussion by an architect of mission architecture as exemplified in the San Xavier del Bac. The volume contains some history.

FORREST, E. R. Missions and pueblos of the old southwest (Cleveland, the Arthur H. Clark company, 1929).

An account of the Spanish missions of New Mexico and Arizona.

FRIAS, HERIBERTO. Leyendas historicas Mexicanas (New York, 1925).

The legendary history of the Aztecs up to the conquest of Mexico by Cortez.

GUERNSEY, A. M. Lands of sunshine (New York, 1916).

HALLENBECK, CLEVE. Spanish missions of the old southwest (New York, 1926).

A brief history of the four southwestern mission fields.

HAMMOND, GEORGE P. Don Juan Oñate and the founding of New Mexico (Santa Fe, 1927).

JAMES, G. WHARTON. In and out of the old missions (Boston, 1922).

This otherwise excellent history of the California missions is somewhat marred by personal bias.

JUDSON, K. B. Myths and legends of California and the old southwest (New York, 1912).

Indian and pioneer stories of California only.

LUMMIS, CHARLES F. The Spanish pioneers (Chicago, 1893).

Lummis has made valuable contributions to the literature of the southwest but they have been biased. This volume contains some historical inaccuracies.

———— Pueblo indian folk stories (New York, 1916).

———— A New Mexico David (New York, 1925).

———— Mesa, canyon, and pueblo (New York, 1925).

———— The land of poco tiempo (New York, 1928).

———— Spanish pioneers and the California missions (New York, 1929).

———— Flowers of our lost romance (New York, 1929).

LUXAN, DIEGO PEREZ DE. Espejo's expedition into New Mexico, 1582-1583. Translated by George P. Hammond and Agapito Rey (Los Angeles, the Quivira society, 1929).

The most reliable of the three existing accounts of Espejo's expedition.

McClintock, J. H. Arizona, prehistoric, aboriginal, pioneer and modern. 3 vols. (Cleveland, 1916).

McGroarty, J. S. California: its history and romance (Los Angeles, 1911).
Entertaining, but not of first rank as history.

Peixotto, E. C. Our Hispanic southwest (New York, 1916).

—— Romantic California (New York, 1914).

Robinson, W. H. Under turquoise skies (New York, 1928).
Three chapters deal with the Spanish frontier.

—— The witchery of Rita (Phoenix, 1919).
A legend of the San Xavier mission in Arizona.

Salpointe, J. B. Soldiers of the cross (New York, 1928).
An account of the southwestern missionary friars.

Sanchez, Nellie van de Grift. Spanish and indian place names of California (San Francisco, 1922).

—— Spanish Arcadia (San Francisco, 1929).

Sturmberg, Robert. History of San Antonio, and the early days in Texas (San Antonio, 1921).

Thomas, A. B. Forgotten frontiers (Norman, Oklahoma, 1932).

Twitchell, R. E. Leading facts of New Mexican history. 5 vols. (Cedar Rapids, 1911-1917).
The first two volumes are historically valuable, the last three merely biographical. Unfortunately the first three centuries of the state's history are compressed into one volume.

Villagra, Gaspar de. Historia de Nuevo Mexico (Alcalá, Spain, 1610).
An account in verse of Oñate's conquest of New Mexico. Recently published in English translation by the Quivira society.

Walter, P. A. F. Cities that died of fear (Santa Fe, 1916).
An account of the abandonment of the Quivira district of New Mexico.

Zavala, Adina de. History and legends of the Alamo and other missions in and around San Antonio (San Antonio, 1920).

Index

Index

Lower California: 40, 45; road through, 49; in legends, 220-225, 227-233, 281

MADONNA: apparition of, 169-176; *see also* Virgin Mary

Malaga (Spain): 127

Manila Galeón: voyages of, 49-50; in legend, 244

Manzanet, Fray Damian: in charge of Texas missions, 29; reports of, 297-298, 302

Margil, Fray Antonio: in legends, 119-126, 305-306

Margil vine: legend, 119-126

Matagorda Bay: 28-29; supplies reach, 31, 128-129, 137; legend referred to, 164

Medina river (Texas): boundary, 34

Mendoza, Antonio de: first viceroy of Mexico, 18; in legend, 62, 71

Mentona, Aguilar: in legend, 110-113

Mentona, Ysabel: in legend, 110-113

Mestizos: 44, 51

Mexico: settlement of, 17-19; visited by Pike, 25; tax on exports to New Mexico, 25; friction with New Mexico, 26; war with Texas, 34; revolution, 43; sells California missions, 45; wins independence, 53; Gadsden purchase, 200-201

Mexico City: captured by Cortez, 18; in legends, 69-72, 217-225, 289-293

Mimbres mountains: 105

Mines: 38, 199-205, 320

Missionaries: 36, character of, 46; in charge of education, 52; killed at Santa Fe, 89; pious fund of, 177-178; mining activities, 199

Missions: established in New Mexico, 23-24; established in Texas, 29-32; disaster strikes in San Antonio valley, 33; remains in Texas, 34-35; established in Arizona, 36-37; abandoned in Arizona, 38-39; remains in Arizona, 39; established in California, 40-41; remains in

California, 43-44; administration of, 44; secularization of, 44-45, 266-274; sale of, 45-46; founded by Kino, 169; erection of San Xavier and others, 177-186; mining activities of, 199-211; San Carlos established, 238-242; *see also* under name of state

Mofras, Capt: 274

Mogollon, Governor-gen: 106-107

Monterey: 41, capital of California, 42; captured by Bouchard, 43; remains of Spanish period in, 44; ships stop at, 49; carriages made, 50; setting of legends, 235-242, 243-253

Monterey Bay: discovered and named by Vizcaino, 40, 236; presidio and mission erected on, 40; in legends, 228-229, 239-242, 243-253

Monterey, Conde de: 217-225, 236

Moors: war with Spain, 86-87, 134

Moquis Indians: pueblos of, 19; characteristics of, 22; mission field extended to, 23; in legends, 67, 93

Moraga, Dorotea: legend of, 187-198

Moraga, Joaquin: *fn* 23; in legend, 187-198

Mount Bonnell: 193

NARVAEZ: expedition of, 19

Nativity, the: reference to, 120-126

Navajos: conflict with Spanish, 24, 109

Navarro: legend of, 139-144

New Albion: named by Drake, 39; English colony in, 227

New Mexico: exploration, 19-21; founding, 21; indian tribes, 21-22; colonization, 23; missions established, 23-24; indian uprisings, 23-25; relations with Mexico, 25-26; captured, 26; monuments of Spanish period, 26-28; Taos fair, 49; colonial life, 46-52; legends, 59-113, 309-310; Santa Clara mission, 96

Teresa of Xeres: in legend, 135-138

Tesuque: in legend, 96

Texas: 24; richest of Spanish possessions, 28; invaded by LaSalle, 28-
29; missions established by Capt.
de Leon, 30; explored by Saint-
Denis, 30; Ramón establishes presidios and missions, 30; conflicts
between French and Spanish in,
31; supplies sent to by water, 31;
missions and settlers in eastern
part transferred, 31; growth of
presidios and missions, 32; disaster
overtakes San Antonio valley, 33;
Spaniards expelled by Anglo-americans, 33-34; war for independence,
34; boundaries of, 34; monuments
of Spanish period, 34-35; colonists
of, 46-52; legends of, 117-164, 306-
308, 319-320; missions in: Bahia,
129-130; Concepción, 35; San Augustine, 298; San Francisco, 35, 100;
San Fernando, 32-35, 139-144, fn
43; San José de Aguayo, 31, 35,
130-134, 135-138, 141; San Juan,
30, 35

Tiguex: in legend, 67-69, 317

Tlascalan Indians: 27; church built
for, 85

Tomas: in legend, 205-211

Tomé (New Mexico): 108

Tompiros: 22; mission field extended
to, 23; in legend, 90-91; see also
Indians

Trade: between Santa Fe and United
States, 25-26; at annual fairs, 49-
50

Trails: see roads

Treasure legends: of Texas, 117;
of Arizona, 199-211; of southwest,
315-321

Trees: 235-242, 259

Tubac presidio: 37-39; legend of,
187-198; illus. front.

Tucson (Arizona): presidio established, 37; withdrawal of garrison,
38

Tumacacori: 202; see also San José
de Tumacacori mission

Tunnels: 305

UNDERGROUND: city, 305

United States: trade with Santa
Fe, 25-26; establishes consulate at
Santa Fe, 26; takes possession of
Arizona, 38; subdues Apaches, 39;
refuses to recognize sale of California missions, 45; Gadsden purchase, 200-201

Utes: conflicts with Spanish, 24, 109

VALDEZ, José: legend of, 306-308

Valdez, Ursula: legend of, 306-308

Vargas, Diego de: captures Santa
Fe, 23-24; governor, 24; buried in
church of San Miguel, 27; in legend, 97-100

Vega, Vincento de la: in legend, 244-
253

Viador, Fray José: legend of, 255-
264

Victoria, Governor: in legend, 271-
274

Virgin Mary: statue of, 98-100; apparitions of, 175-176, 290-293

Vizcaino, Sebastian: voyage up Pacific coast, 40, 236-237; legend of
expedition, 217-225

WARFARE: in New Mexico, 24-25;
France-Spain, 31; in Texas, 32; in
Arizona, 37, 38-39; Moors and
Spain, 86-87, 134

Wedding: first in Texas, 30

Wichita Indians: conflicts with Spanish, 32

XERES (Spain): in legend, 135, 137

YE, JUAN: in legend, 98

Yellowstone Park: explored by Spaniards, 25

Ytur Yupiha: in legend, 147-154

Yumas: characteristics, 36-37; con-